ENVIRONMENTAL PROTECTION: NEW APPROACHES

ENVIRONMENTAL PROTECTION: NEW APPROACHES

JOHN E. BLODGETT

Novinka Books
New York

Library of Congress Cataloging-in-Publication Data
Available Upon Request

ISBN: 1-59033-744-1.

Nova Science Publishers, Inc.
400 Oser Ave, Suite 1600
Hauppauge, New York 11788-3619
Tele. 631-231-7269 Fax 631-231-8175
e-mail: Novascience@earthlink.net
Web Site: http://www.novapublishers.com

Printed in the United States of America

CONTENTS

FOREWORD*

In recent years, the interest in alternatives to the nation's "command-and- control" approach to environmental protection has heightened. Driving this interest are concerns that the current approach is inefficient and excessively costly, and that it is ineffective in addressing certain problems such as nonpoint source pollution and global climate change. Several blue-ribbon panels have issued reports on environmental protection needs for the next century, including one headed by former two-time Administrator of the Environmental Protection Agency, William D. Ruckelshaus - *The Environmental Protection System in Transition: Toward a More Desirable Future* (1998)- and one by the National Academy of Public Administration - www.environment.com: *Transforming Environmental Protection for the 21st Century* (2000).

Alternative environmental protection approaches range from proposals that would replace the current system to ones that would supplement it. Elements of the proposals include enhanced information processes, greater reliance on market mechanisms, devolution of federal responsibilities to state and local decisionmakers, and substitution of private markets for public actions. The proposals for the most part represent a mix of techniques, and few are really new. Most of the ideas have been developed and promoted for some time; many have been incorporated to some degree in existing programs.

This book summarizes briefly a number of "new approaches," grouped under the following categories:

---

* This book is excerpted from CRS Report RL30760.

- Information: Approaches to improve the quantity and quality of information to enhance the knowledge base underlying environmental decisions (e.g., risk assessment, cost-benefit analysis).

- Public Sector Processes: Approaches to restructure governmental processes for making environmental decisions (e.g., devolution).

- Incentives: Approaches that emphasize incentives as opposed to regulatory or financial penalties for achieving environmental ends.

- Market Mechanisms: Approaches that rely on markets and common law for environmental decisions to the extent possible.

- Management Principles: Approaches to inculcate environmental values in public or private managerial decisions (e.g., sustainability).

Each approach seems to have some useful applications. Each has some disciplinary, ideological, or institutional proponent; but none commands the multi- stakeholder commitment necessary for truly transforming environmental programs. There may be consensus that environmental protection programs could and should be improved, but beyond modest iterative steps, there is as yet no consensus on what that would entail nor on how to achieve those steps. Critical to this lack of consensus is an apparent split in proponents' goals - those most focused on improving the efficiency of the current process, versus those most focused on finding new ways to address so-far intractable environmental problems such as global climate change.

Chapter 1

INTRODUCTION[1]

Since the early 1970s, as U.S. environmental policy burgeoned, a key debate has centered on the proper approach for federal environmental protection programs. The dominant approach of choice has been a regulatory one - often labeled "command and control"[2] - in which government decisionmakers set standards or specify particular actions required of potential or actual polluters. However, concerns about economic inefficiency, the difficulty of addressing certain problems such as nonpoint source pollution, and other perceived shortcomings of the regulatory approach have from the beginning stimulated interest in alternative environmental protection approaches that would complement, supplement, or even replace the regulatory regime.

In recent years, the interest in alternatives has taken on a new intensity. Several reasons explain this interest, including: First, while the regulatory approach has been quite successful in reducing pollution originating from large point sources - such as manufacturing facilities and sewage outfalls - as well as pollution arising from products with relatively few manufacturers - such as automobiles and pesticides - it has not been so successful in addressing "nonpoint" sources of pollution, such as agricultural and urban runoff, nor small "dispersed" sources, from domestic fireplaces to small

---

[1] Prepared by John E. Blodgett, Deputy Assistant Director, Resources, Science, and Industry Division, Congressional Research Service.

[2] For an introduction to the early development of environmental protection programs, see Frank P. Grad, et al., Environmental Control: Priorities, Policies, and the Law (New York: Columbia University Press, 1971), especially pp. 47-183. For an assessment of why market mechanisms were not more readily adopted during that early development, see Steven Kelman, What Price Incentives? Economists and the Environment (Boston: Auburn House Publishing Company, 1981).

businesses. Second, economic and other analyses have suggested that, compared to regulation, various alternative approaches may be more economically efficient and may encourage technological developments to reduce pollution, among other advantages. Third, the federal "command and control" approach troubles those concerned about the overall size and power of the federal government. Fourth, some argue that the regulatory approach has become captured by one or another set of stakeholders. Some environmentalists believe that those being regulated strongly influence the process, to the detriment of the environment, while others perceive regulators as overly responsive to environmentalists. Additionally, the advent of a new millennium has seemed, at least to some, a propitious symbolic opportunity for exploring alternatives. (For selected initiatives and publications relating to the future of environmental protection, see Appendix A.)

Numerous alternative environmental protection approaches have been proposed. They range from proposals that would radically reshape the environmental protection approach in the nation, to proposals that would fine-tune existing programs. Metaphorically, some proposals represent new tool boxes for addressing environmental problems, others represent individual new tools. Generally, they are not exclusive; that is, any environmental protection program would likely draw on a mix of the tools. Moreover, their "newness" lies more in application than conception: most of these ideas have been developed and promoted for some time; many have been incorporated to some degree in existing programs.

Chapter 2

ENVIRONMENTAL MANAGEMENT: A PORTFOLIO OF "NEW" TOOLS

This book summarizes briefly a number of "new approaches," grouped under the following categories:

- Information: Approaches to improve the quantity and quality of information and to organize it effectively so as to enhance the knowledge base underlying decisions affecting the environment

- Public Sector Processes: Approaches to revise or create new governmental structures or processes for making environmental decisions

- Incentives: Approaches that emphasize incentives as opposed to regulatory or financial penalties for achieving environmental ends

- Market Mechanisms: Approaches that rely on markets and common law for environmental decisions to the extent possible

- Management Principles: Approaches to inculcate environmental values in public and private managerial decisions

These categories are not necessarily mutually exclusive. Not only may the approaches overlap, but also the various "tools" may serve more than one approach. As will become apparent, the idea of a "new approach" to environmental management in reality consists of a mix of ideas and proposals.

INFORMATION

This group of approaches centers on enhancing the information available to decision-makers, including administrators, legislators, environmental managers, polluters, and the public. Legislatively establishing information generating processes is not novel, of course. It is the essence of the National Environmental Policy Act of 1969 (NEPA, P.L. 91-190), specifically the "environmental impact statements" (EIS) provision of section 102, which requires a study of environmental effects of alternative approaches to federal actions. Initially, there was a question of whether the EIS requirement of NEPA applied to environmental regulatory decisions; in the end, only selected environmental regulatory decisions were made subject to the EIS requirement. Proposals for cost-benefit analyses, risk assessments, and the use of "sound science" represent continuing pressure for generating and/or arranging information to improve decisionmaking. Within this group of information tools are a number that proponents believe will benefit decision-making in various ways.

- In general - "Sound Science"[3]

- Information focused on improving regulatory decisions, in particular risk analysis and cost-benefit analysis

- Information focused on improving planner/program manager decisions, in particular "green accounting" and materials accounting/materials management

- Information focused on improving consumer/voter decisions, in particular the Toxic Release Inventory and energy efficiency ratings

Often these proposals to enhance information for environmental decisions are proffered with the stated goal of improving regulatory decisions; certainly this has been the primary impetus for developing cost-benefit analysis and risk assessment, and for much of the concern about

[3] Items in bold are discussed at length in the body of the report.

"sound science." Some alternatives to regulation may reduce the need for certain kinds of information. For example, a pollution tax may generate a price signal that leads to pollution controls without the government needing information on the specific controls used, as might be required by regulation. On the other hand, the alternative may require its own enhanced information base; thus, implementing a pollution tax could depend on developing particular information in order to set such a tax at an appropriate level. (It should be noted that reliable information may be costly to collect, maintain, and interpret and may raise issues of confidentiality.)

Public Sector Processes

This second set of approaches proposes to improve environmental decisions by restructuring the processes by which those decisions are made in the public sector. Proposals include:

- Environmental Federalism - state delegation -defederalism/ devolution - "Civic Environmentalism"
- Creation of an independent cost-benefit/risk assessment review body
- Establishment of a "Regulatory Budget"

These proposals are designed primarily to reform and improve the regulatory process, not to replace it.

Incentives

A third set of approaches seeks to shift the emphasis from a government regulatory role with its enforcement and compliance emphasis to a supportive role based on incentives to encourage environmentally beneficial actions. These include:

- Grants, loans, tax breaks
- Procurement policies

- Technical assistance
- Regulatory waivers, "Beyond compliance"

If the role of government in a regulatory approach is that of the "stick," then for these alternatives the role of government is to offer "carrots." Inducements can include the provision of information; technical and financial support; or regulatory relief for voluntary compliance, especially if it goes beyond what might be required. Typically, incentive approaches leave the potential or actual polluter to respond as he or she chooses - that is, to decide whether to seek out and use assistance, or to decide whether the amount of reimbursement for costs of pollution-reducing actions is worth it. The conduct of research and development, to develop information and techniques, might be seen as an indispensable antecedent to governmental incentive programs.

Market Mechanisms

This set of approaches shifts as much as possible of the decisionmaking on environmental protection away from the government to the private sector:

- Market mechanisms by which environmental standards can be met, including trading, banking, and offsetting of pollution rights; and the "clean development mechanism," to allow international trading
- Market signals, such as through pollution taxes and liability risks under tort law (plus information such as from the Toxic Release Inventory)
- Private markets/private property, including common law remedies, trespass protections, and "free market environmentalism"

What distinguishes all of these alternatives is the reliance on marketplace-type processes to affect decisions with respect to their environmental implications. A potential or actual polluter can decide what action is best, given his or her circumstances, based on emission allowances (e.g., in a banking/trading program); cost signals (e.g., from a pollution tax); liability from imposed risks (e.g., from harm resulting from waste disposal practices); or liability from violating private property rights (e.g., when pollution crosses property lines). For these alternatives, the role of government lies primarily in setting the rules and boundaries on the market, and/or establishing the courts and rules of evidence for determining legal redress. In contrast to the regulatory approach, the government does relatively less specking of environmental requirements that designated sources would have to meet, although a standards-setting role may be maintained.

MANAGEMENT PRINCIPLES

A fifth group of approaches relies on defining management processes or values that proponents believe would result in good environmental outcomes:

- "Sustainability"
- Precautionary principle
- Ecosystem management
- Environmental Management Systems
- Pollution prevention
- Certification
- "Good Management Practices"

Where the privatizing approach would affect decisions concerning the environment by modifying market signals, the management process approach proposes to affect decisions by promoting and reinforcing environmentally oriented values. Generally, "good management" approaches have entailed moral suasion, sometimes backed with incentives; they are often seen as a "voluntary" alternative to regulatory mandates. A key issue is who can and should define such standards; typical options include governmental bodies (international, federal, state, local), professional societies, and private sector consortia. Experience suggests that translating general values of environmental protection into practical decisionmaking is not always easy, however. In a regulatory setting, incentives may be contingent on complying with the standards; in other contexts, compliance may be largely or entirely voluntary.

Chapter 3

SELECTING AND IMPLEMENTING NEW APPROACHES

What is striking about these proposals for complementing, supplementing, or replacing environmental regulation is how few of them are really new, and how even fewer represent radically new approaches. In part, this may simply reflect the truth that there is nothing new under the sun; but even more, it may reflect the fact the environmental protection system that has grown up over the past 40 years in the U.S., while dominated by a federal regulatory approach, consists of complex, multifaceted, and interlocking institutions, laws, regulations, and programs involving all levels of government. Some aspects of virtually every approach proposed have found at least some niche for trial, and some are, in fact, widely accepted as practical for particular applications. (For example, the market approach of the acid rain program under the Clean Air Act is widely viewed as greatly successful and as a potential model for additional programs; but it is not widely viewed as a model for comprehensively replacing the existing environmental regulatory regimen. Likewise, the Toxic Release Inventory is widely viewed as a greatly successful informational mechanism, but whether it should be expanded is highly contentious.)

For those proposing different environmental protection approaches, the quest for alternatives is often driven by a conviction that the existing system is piecemeal, unduly complex, inefficient, and too costly. Implicitly, this view suggests that a new approach would be simpler, neater, more efficient, and hence less costly - and surely more (cost)-effective. This search for more efficient, less costly approaches has focused on market alternatives because traditional economic analysis suggests that market-based alternatives are usually more efficient. However, empirically, the relative efficiencies may not always be clear-cut.[4] Moreover, while the ideas for "new alternatives" to regulation have attracted much attention and considerable theoretical analysis, assessments of the actual costs to develop and implement them are often lacking. Even where alternatives may in the long run save money - for example in private sector compliance costs- they may require substantial up-front investments, often by government at some level.[5]

One recent effort to examine program and policy alternatives was the Enterprise for the Environment (E4E) project, headed by former EPA Administrator William Ruckelshaus. Basically, the E4E project concluded that there was no single new environmental protection approach; rather, the participants concluded that the "existing system must be improved" through an iterative, "deliberate, step-by-step process" that involves better information, flexibility, best-available scientific and economic information, and a "broad set of policy tools."[6] As Ruckelshaus said in his preface –

> None of us were so certain that we knew how to construct the new system that we were willing to recommend its immediate adoption; we recognized that a lot of care and adaptive management will be needed along the way. Thus we were led to recommend a "stepping-stone" approach, one that allows us to move carefully and systematically from where we are today to where we want to go.[7]

Further impetus for the quest for a new approach arises from the recognition that the present system seems ill-equipped to deal with some important environmental problems - some of long standing concern, like nonpoint source pollution, others more newly recognized, such as global climate change. These problems have proved extremely difficult, especially where they involve individual behaviors on the one hand, and where they

---

[4] See Robert W. Hahn, "The Impact of Economics on Environmental Policy," Journal of Environmental Economics and Management, 39 (May 2000), 375-399.

[5] See, for example, the conclusion of Rena I. Steinzor, "The Corruption of Civic Environmentalism," Environmental Law Reporter, V. XXX, no. 10 (Oct. 2000), 10921:"... there can be little doubt that civic environmentalism will be a more expensive alternative [than the regulatory system], if it is carried out in accordance with the civic environmentalists' stated goals. Gathering and organizing the information necessary to impose effective performance-based standards will be very expensive, as will the financial support that should be provided to level the playing field' for local groups. "This then brings us to what is, in many ways, the ultimate dilemma. As long as we are in the throes of denying that reinvention will cost money, we will not end up with reinvention as advocated...."

[6] The Environmental Protection System in Transition: Toward a More Desirable Future (Washington, D.C.: Center for Strategic and International Studies. 1998), pp. 3, 5,4.

[7] Ibid., p. viii.

involve global actions on the other. The E4E project concluded that tackling these issues was beyond its capabilities.[8]

A second major effort to examine program and policy alternatives was a series of studies by the National Academy of Public Administration (NAPA), culminating in a report environment.gov: *Transforming Environmental Protection for the 21st Century*.[9] In many respects, the NAPA report comes to similar conclusions as the E4E project (not so surprisingly, as Ruckelshaus was on the Panel that prepared it). The report begins by defining three high-priority environmental protection problems for which the existing regulatory system is proving inadequate and for which the report recommends innovative, alternative approaches. These three problems are:

- nutrient pollution of waters, mainly from nonpoint sources;
- dispersed sources of ground-level ozone and smog; and
- global climate change.

The NAPA report directly discusses the need for statutory changes, particularly to allow innovation, to increase flexibility among media-focused programs, and to develop better information on environmental quality.

The report analyzes the successes and failures of efforts to make environmental protection programs more efficient and effective.[10] It assessed the respective roles of all levels of government, business and industry, the public, and the Congress. The report concludes that the nation will continue to need a strong national environmental regulatory agency; that the agency needs both to adopt innovations to achieve more efficient environmental protection and to take a leadership role in developing alternatives (especially market mechanisms) and in mobilizing public and congressional support for them; and that the federal government needs to be a leader in providing credible, authoritative environmental information.

While E4E and the NAPA Report focus on environmental protection, the development of the concept "sustainability," originating in global concerns, subsumes environmental protection issues within a broader

---

[8] Ibid. In the end, virtually all the environmental stakeholders originally participating in the E4E process dropped out. One of the main reasons was that they felt the process was failing to address continuing and emerging environmental problems.

[9] Published by the National Academy of Public Administration, 2000. Two earlier reports by the Academy were Setting Priorities, Getting Results: A New Direction for EPA, and Resolving the Paradox of Environmental Protection: An Agenda for Congress, EPA and the States. These reports were funded by Congress through appropriations to EPA.

[10] NAPA commissioned 17 research papers relating to environmental protection innovation: see Appendix A of environment.com.

framework of long-term resource management. The term "sustainable development" emerged in its current form in 1987 in the final report of the United Nations World Commission on Environment and Development (WCED).[11] The definition most widely quoted in the WCED report is: "Development that meets the needs of the present without compromising the ability of future generations to meet their own needs." The importance of the concept is that traditional economic analysis often treats growth in economic activity without taking into account possible deterioration of the resource base; sustainability analysis focuses on the ability of resources to sustain economic activity over the long-run. In this context, pollution becomes viewed as a degrader of the resource base.

Finally, concerns about the federal role itself can drive the search for a new environmental protection approach. For some, the federal government is simply too big and too powerful. They would cut down the federal environmental role, typically relying on state programs, the marketplace, and/or tort and common law to resolve environmental problems. For some others, the federal regulatory process has been captured by one or another set of stakeholders - for some, the polluters, for others, environmentalists. Their response often involves radical restructuring not just of environmental protection programs, but of all governing institutions.

The existing system is embedded in law, institutions, and expectations. Its inertia must be overcome to accomplish change, modification, or even improvement. Overall, while each "approach" could contribute to protecting the environment, none seems to command an essential breadth of political and technical respect to be seen as a single viable "new direction" for the 21st Century. Each "approach" seems to have some useful application. Each has some disciplinary, ideological, or institutional proponent; indeed, many of the approaches have become virtually inseparable from the institutions and/or group of individuals promoting them.

While many have contributed to the conceptual development of alternative approaches, the largest share has come from the work of academics and think tanks. Institutions involved in international development issues have also contributed, such as the Organization for Economic Co-operation and Development (OECD). Business and industry interests have more commonly reacted to regulatory issues than taken the

[11] World Commission on Environment and Development, Our Common Future (Oxford: Oxford University Press, 1987).

lead in conceptualizing new approaches.[12] Environmental and health public interest groups have more commonly focused on the need to address environmental problems than on the development of new approaches. The White House's Council on Environmental Quality- a dynamic force in environmental policy development in the early 1970s - has been allowed to atrophy. And the Environmental Protection Agency - whose Administrator the NAPA report suggests might spearhead the transformation of environmental policy in the 21st Century -has tended to focus on finetuning the existing system. Indeed, it was Congress through the appropriations process that directed the Agency to contract with NAPA to prepare the analyses that led to *environment, corn: Transforming Environmental Protection for the 21st Century.*

What it would take to prompt additional innovation is the question: it could be a crisis - perhaps a critical environmental threat for which regulation seems powerless or some fundamental environmental regulatory mistake that threatens economic disaster. Alternatively, it might be, as the NAPA report urges, a sustained initiative by the future head of EPA, the new President, and/or the Congress. Absent a crisis or this kind of initiative, it is hard to see how the regulatory "approach" will be supplanted generally until amore comprehensive, interdisciplinary, multi-stakeholder commitment to some alternative emerges. That, indeed, would seem to be the final lesson of the E4E and the NAPA projects: there maybe consensus that environmental protection programs could and should be improved, but beyond modest iterative steps, there is as yet no consensus on what that would entail nor on how to achieve those steps.

Building toward that consensus would appear to be the next necessary step if environmental policy is to be transformed. Inhibiting the formation of consensus is a split in the way proponents tend to see new approaches: for some they are primarily ways to solve the inefficiencies of the existing regulatory problem; for others they are primarily ways to address unresolved or new environmental problems. Those focused on inefficiency fear that expanding environmental protections to new problems would make the burdens of compliance worse; while those focused on environmental insults fear that efforts to reduce inefficiencies would be accomplished by retreating

---

[12] See, however, the works of Stephan Schmidheiny, e.g.. Financing Change: The Financial Community, Eco-efficiency, and Sustainable Development (Cambridge, Mass.: MIT Press, 1996).

from environmental protections and ignoring new problems. These divergent motives inhibit joint recognition of opportunities for new approaches to contribute both to efficiency and to effectiveness.

Chapter 4

SELECTED NEW APPROACHES TO ENVIRONMENTAL PROTECTION

The remainder of this report consists of brief introductions to selected new approaches to environmental protection. Each identifies a tool, or set of related tools, describes its basic characteristics, notes "pros" and "cons" associated with the tool, provides some background, summarizes current developments, and concludes with a list of readings for further research. These introductions are necessarily brief and incomplete; their purpose is to expose the reader to these alternatives and to provide sources through which the reader can pursue ideas that he or she finds promising.

INFORMATION

Making environmental decisions requires an understanding of the problem at hand and the ability to predict outcomes from alternative actions. Common criticisms of the existing regulatory approach to environmental management are that decisionmakers may lack sufficient, reliable information to make a sound decision; that they may rely on invalid data or findings or selectively choose only data supporting preferred outcomes (i.e., "junk science"); or that they may rely overmuch on nontechnical determinants at the expense of sound scientific information. A presumption that sufficient, robust information will be brought to bear objectively on environmental decisions underlies all conceptions of an improved or alternative approach. What this presumption means in general is often subsumed in calls for "sound science"; particular applications include risk analysis and cost-benefit analysis, among other methods of generating and organizing information.

"Sound Science"[13]

The idea of "sound science" encompasses at least two parts of the policy decisionmaking process. The first part is establishing the technical knowledge underlying the issue and assessing possible solutions. This involves many activities, including development, validation, and application of research methods; environmental monitoring; epidemiological studies; data collection, storage, and evaluation; laboratory experiments; integration of disciplinary knowledge; and assessment of the robustness of the data, experimental results, and interpretive findings.

The second part of science-in-policy is applying the scientific understanding to the policy issue. At this intersection of science and policy, of scientists and decisionmakers, the question about the science moves from "What do we know?" to "What do these findings mean (in terms of the policy options faced by the decisionmaker)?" To illustrate, science can address the question, "At a 95% confidence level, what is the no-effect level of arsenic in drinking water?"; the policy question might be, "What level of exposure to arsenic in drinking water will we consider safe?" Or, scientifically, "What do we know about the effects of emissions of mercury from fossil fuel combustion?", where the policy question might be, "Should emissions of mercury be regulated?" While sound science may necessarily underlie a good policy decision, it is not sufficient: statutory and administrative requirements and social and cultural values are also determinative.

Validating and Applying Science

Because policy issues by definition involve conflicting viewpoints, both the validity of the science base as well as its interpretation may be challenged. Scientists have developed processes for ensuring robust results - that is, scientific information that is widely perceived as reliable. Crucial components of these processes include publication of both data and results so experiments can be independently repeated to verify results, and peer review through which colleagues assess and, at times, challenge findings and interpretations. Science is not static: new observations and understandings

[13] Prepared by Michael Simpson, Specialist in Life Sciences, and John E. Blodgett, Deputy Assistant Director, Resources, Science, and Industry Division.

may raise questions about the findings of earlier studies, and peer review and the self-correcting nature of science help ensure that scientific knowledge is updated to reflect the most current and widely-accepted thinking in the scientific community. Thus scientific knowledge is always subject to some degree of uncertainty, especially in frontier areas such as ecology and the environment. Even widely agreed-upon scientific findings may be accompanied by "loose ends": incomplete data as well as some data that do not fit, uncertainties, probabilistic findings, ranges in results, incomplete studies, and not infrequently, some contradictory findings and even an occasional reputable scientist who contends in favor of an alternative conclusion.

The policymaker - usually not a scientist - must meld the technical information with the other factors involved in his or her decision. Even if the science indicates a problem, it may not indicate a solution. The EPA Administrator's 1998 decision to set a very fine particulate matter (PM) National Ambient Air Quality Standard is illustrative: while 19 out of 21 members of the Clean Air Scientific Advisory Committee recommended that EPA regulate PM the body fragmented on what level would be appropriate for the standard. Thus, in setting a standard, the Administrator must not only make decisions about the "loose ends" of the scientific findings, but also must incorporate appropriate policy determinants - from the statutory guidelines to social ethos. Claims of "junk science" can stem both from disagreements concerning a decisionmaker's handling of uncertainties and any persisting scientific "loose ends" and from disagreements about the need for and effectiveness of alternative solutions.

Uncertainty

Perhaps the single biggest challenge to the decisionmaker is deciding when the robustness of the science outweighs remaining uncertainties. The question of when enough reliable information is available to act is, in the end, a policy call. As an emerging arena of scientific attention, environmental issues have regularly been bedeviled by that question: notable examples include DDT and its effects on birds, PCBs and their persistence in the environment, emissions causing acid rain, and the hypothesis that chlorofluorocarbons deteriorate stratospheric ozone; and it continues at the center of the climate change debate.

For scientists, uncertainty can be an opportunity for further research; for policymakers, uncertainty is a void that makes assessing options more difficult. But more research takes time - and during that time further damages may occur. This raises the policy question. In the face of potential but uncertain hazards, should one defer action until better information is at hand, or should one act quickly to forestall possible future damages? In part, the answer depends on the risks and costs involved, but there are other considerations, as well. A key concern is who will generate the better information - Should that be a government responsibility, or should it be the responsibility of the producer of the hazard, if identifiable? One management principle for dealing with uncertainty is the "Precautionary Principle," discussed below.

Federal Procedures

Congress and the Administration have developed a number of procedures and processes to ensure that the scientific underpinnings of environmental, health, and safety decisions are robust, and that policy decisions are sound. These include:

- creation of scientific bodies to advise policymakers: government-wide ones include the federally-chartered National Academy of Sciences - National Research Council and the Office of Science and Technology Policy in the Executive Office of the President; individual agencies have their own science advisory bodies, for example the Science Advisory Board appointed by the Administrator of EPA, as well as specialized ones, such as the Clean Air Scientific Advisory Committee in EPA mandated by the Clean Air Act

- employment of scientific research expertise within agencies (including the Department of Agriculture, Food and Drug Administration, and Environmental Protection Agency), or in parallel to the administrative body (Occupational Safety and Health Administration - National Institute for Occupational Safety and Health)

- statutory and/or administrative requirements for incorporating science in policymaking decisions, for example the criteria document review process spelled out in the Clean Air Act, plus a statutory requirement that scientific data generated through federal research dollars be publicly available:[14] as well as requirements in

[14] Generated by a controversy over the availability for review of data used in assessing health risks from air pollution.

the Administrative Procedure Act (5 U.S.C. 551 et seq.) for public review of administrative decisions (for air quality regulations, these are replaced by special administrative review procedures in the Clean Air Act [42 U.S.C. 7607(d)]); Executive Order 12866, *Regulatory Planning and Review*, requires that "Each agency shall base its [regulatory] decisions on die best reasonably obtainable scientific, technical, economic, and other information concerning the need for, and consequences of, the intended regulation" (Sec. 1 (b)(7)).

Both improvements to environmental regulatory programs and the development of alternative environmental management techniques presume continued enhancement of the science underpinning decisions. How to ensure sound science has attracted congressional attention, notably in the context of various controversial EPA regulatory actions, and most particularly with respect to oversight of EPA's 1998 ozone and fine particulates National Ambient Air Quality Standards.[15] Most proposals to reform and improve EPA's regulations would mandate cost-benefit analysis and/or risk assessment procedures - which themselves depend on good scientific information - to enhance the information base for decisions. Some regulatory reform bills also specifically provide for new mechanisms to enhance the science underlying regulatory decisionmaking-e.g., in the 106th Congress, H.R. 574, introduced by Rep. Pombo, would require peer review of scientific data used in support of federal regulations through establishment of a list of impartial peer reviewers from which agency heads would select reviewers for comment on proposed regulations; H.R.5195, introduced by Rep. Ehlers, would provide for the establishment of a position of Deputy Administrator for Science and Technology of the Environmental Protection Agency.

---

15 E.g., U.S. Congress, House, Committee on Science, Subcommittee on Energy and Environment, The Science behind the Environmental Protection Agency's (EPA 's) Proposed Revisions to the National Ambient Air Quality Standards for Ozone and Particulate Matter, Parts 1-111, Hearings [No. 21] (105th Cong., Ist sess.) (Washington, D.C.: U.S. Govt. Print. Off., 1997), 659 pp.

Risk Analysis[16]

Risk analysis is a tool for setting priorities among programs and evaluating management options. In the context of environmental issues, "risk" is defined as the probability of occurrence of a particular adverse effect on human health or the environment as a result of exposure to a "hazard," which may be a chemical, some other technology, or a natural hazard, such as flooding. "Risk assessment" refers to a formal or informal procedure producing a quantitative estimate of environmental risk. For example, risk assessment is often used to estimate the expected rate of illness or death in a population exposed to a hazardous chemical. "Risk analysis" is used more broadly to include quantitative and qualitative evaluation of all relevant attributes of environmental hazards, risks, adverse effects, events and conditions that lead to or modify adverse effects, and populations or environments that influence or experience adverse effects. Comparative (or relative) risk analysis and cost-benefit analysis are aids to risk management, the process of deciding what should be done about hazards, for example, to reduce risk.

Thus, risk analysis is a tool for risk management, and Environmental Protection Agency risk managers increasingly have relied on it, to the extent permitted by law. In setting priorities across or within program offices, EPA sometimes has compared risks or risk reduction potential of different regulatory targets. In developing regulations, EPA has used the results of risk analysis to set standards, to compare the effectiveness of various control measures, and to evaluate risks relative to costs. Risks avoided (i.e., the difference between risks before and risks after a regulation is implemented) are the usual measure of benefits for environmental or health and safety regulations. Reports by the Commission on Risk Assessment and Risk Management[17] and the National Academy of Public Administration[18] recommend an expanded role for risk analysis in risk management.

Benefits and Costs of Risk Analysis

Environmental risk analysis assists decisionmakers by summarizing available data about hazards and potential effects of exposure. At its best,

---

[16] Prepared by Linda-Jo Schierow, Specialist in Environmental Policy, Resources, Science, and Industry Division, Congressional Research Service.

[17] The Presidential/Congressional Commission on Risk Assessment and Risk Management, Framework for Environmental Health Risk Management (Vol. 1) and Risk Assessment and Risk Management in Regulatory Decision-Making (Vol. 2) (Washington, D.C.: 1997).

[18] Setting Priorities, Getting Results: A New Direction for the Environmental Protection Agency (Washington, D.C.: National Academy of Public Administration, 1995).

when reliable data are available, scientific understanding is relatively advanced, methods are reliable (i.e., when the underlying science is sound), and interested stakeholders are involved in the process, risk analysis can facilitate decisions. Quantified, robust information about alternative regulatory strategies and their potential consequences - implementation and compliance costs, risks avoided, and other benefits - help policymakers and the general public set priorities, allocate resources, assess options, and evaluate existing federal laws and programs. Also, it is a critical component of cost-benefit analysis.

Risk assessment is not always at its best, however: the scientific understanding of a risk may be undeveloped, data incomplete, and experiments unfruitful; practitioners and stakeholders may disagree on methods and interpretations. Ensuring that the underlying science for risk assessment is sound requires resources - time, effort, and money - to collect data, conduct experiments, run computer models, analyze findings, and write reports. Agency resources expended on analysis may not be available for enforcement, program evaluation, or research. Some costs, for example, collection of data, maybe shifted to those regulated; for example, the Clean Air Act requires large emitters of certain air pollutants to monitor emissions. Another concern has been that the time required to conduct risk analysis may make difficult the meeting of deadlines for implementation of provisions of major environmental statutes. Finally, quantitative risk assessment, by focusing on the data that do exist and on risks that are best understood, may thereby ignore or insufficiently account for other risk parameters. For example, many environmentalists, among others, have long been concerned that risk assessment often over-weighs cancer endpoints compared to other health risks; and it often over-weighs health endpoints generally compared to ecological risks.

Executive and Legislative Interest in Risk Analysis

The potential value of risk assessment has both stimulated research in its development and made its use a focus of policy debates. Presidents have attempted to encourage more consistent use of risk and economic analysis by federal agencies through executive orders. Most recently, President Clinton's Executive Order 12866 requires EPA to analyze risks, costs, and benefits for "significant" rules, including all proposed and final rules expected to cost at least $100 million in a year.

Congress also has issued general mandates to federal agencies to encourage greater use of risk and cost-benefit analysis. The Unfunded Mandates Reform Act (P.L. 104-4), Title II, requires all federal agencies to quantitatively assess benefits, including the effect of a federal mandate on health, safety, and the natural environment, and to compare benefits to costs for all rules with an expected cost of $100 million or more in a year. However, of 110 economically significant rules promulgated in the first 2 years since enactment, 78 did not require assessments due to specific exemptions allowed by the Act, according to the U. S. General Accounting Office.

The 104th Congress added mandates for considering risks to two environmental statutes authorizing EPA's regulatory activities, the Federal Insecticide, Fungicide, and Rodenticide Act and the Safe Drinking Water Act. The 105th and 106th Congresses have continued working on legislation that would foster and in some cases require more rigorous use of risk assessment by regulatory agencies. For example, S. 746 (Levin-Thompson), the Regulatory Improvement Act of 1999 [106th Congress] would codify the requirements for cost-benefit analysis and risk assessment for major rules, and executive oversight of the rulemaking process. Among its major provisions, the bill would have required regulatory agencies to prepare a risk assessment if rule involves a risk to health, safety, or the environment; provide for independent peer review of risk assessments and cost-benefit analyses for rules costing $500 million; and include cost-benefit analysis, cost-benefit determinants, and risk assessment in the rulemaking record. The Office of Information and Regulatory Affairs, in consultation with the Office of Science and Technology Policy, would issue guidelines for risk assessments.

Cost-Benefit Analysis[19]

Cost-benefit analysis is one way to organize, evaluate, and present information about the actions that governments take to improve public well-being. With respect to environmental and health issues, risk assessment, which presents information in such terms as morbidity and mortality for humans or animals, is a prerequisite for cost-benefit analysis, which places monetary values on attributes of human well-being.[20] And like risk assessment, its use can be complicated, expensive, and controversial.

---

[19] Prepared by John L. Moore, Assistant Director, Resources, Science and Industry Division.

[20] Risk assessors tend to be drawn from various health and environmental disciplines, including epidemiology, toxicology, statistics, public health, and others; cost-benefit analysis is primarily the domain of economics.

As a set of procedures to measure the merit of some public sector actions in dollar terms, cost-benefit analysis is a counterpart to private-sector profitability accounting. The difference is that most public actions to improve public well-being do not have established private markets which generate price information on which to judge their value or benefits. To compare the public benefit of such actions to their costs, benefits (and sometimes costs) are indirectly estimated in dollar terms. The objective is to determine the alternative for public action that produces the largest net gain to the society. In this case, gain is not in terms of private sector profit, but rather as an estimated surplus of monetized benefits over estimated costs. Based on this criterion, cost-benefit analysis attempts to identify the most economically efficient way of meeting a public objective. Other goals of public management are not focused on in this process, but in some cases they may be subsumed in the analysis.

The debate over cost-benefit analysis focuses on its possible value in reducing the perceived economic burden and complexity of traditional regulatory approaches. Greater use of cost-benefit analysis is part of the broader regulatory reform effort calling for increased flexibility in regulatory approaches and increased accountability and scrutiny of regulatory decisions.

Complexities

Formal cost-benefit analysis often demands costly and sometimes disputed expertise and data. Done carefully, it provides an array of information that can inform the decision process. Done poorly or taken out of context, the results can create a false sense of clarity and precision. Methods, data, expense, and prospects for court challenges on use and abuse are concerns driving debate on how greater use of this tool may figure in regulatory reform.

The tensions in regulatory reform and the role of cost-benefit analysis touch on many complex issues. These include: scientific capabilities in measuring and characterizing long-term and often uncertain health, safety, and environmental phenomena; agency capacity for collecting and using data; methods to characterize positive and negative effects of regulations; equity in protecting the public against health, safety, and environmental risks; burdens on lower levels of government and the private sector in achieving public goals; and fundamental questions of regulatory design such as flexibility and location of implementing and decisionmaking authority.

The role and application of cost-benefit analysis by agencies are important focuses of the evolving process of regulatory reform.

Disagreements typically revolve around the practicality and usefulness of strict application of the tool. The conflicts involve more questions of "how much" and "to what end" than "whether," since these techniques are already used by federal agencies to differing degrees in assessing many of their regulatory activities.

Application of Cost-Benefit Analysis: Support and Criticism

Cost-benefit can be applied to public actions using varying degrees of formality (how far analysts go in trying to compare monetized benefits with costs). At one level, some believe that the only regulations that should be maintained or adopted are those that clearly pass the cost-benefit test - namely, benefits must demonstrably exceed the costs. Proponents of this position argue that promulgating only those regulations where benefits outweigh or justify costs (presumably in monetary terms) can help rationalize the regulatory process and improve priority setting. In this view, such reform would increase the likelihood that regulations will not place burdens on businesses and consumers that are out of proportion to gains in health, safety, or environmental protection. Such a change, it is maintained, could lead to more systematic consideration of more efficient ways to achieve desirable health, safety, and environmental protection goals. Excessive regulations would be minimized, eliminating rules and enforcement where goals are ill defined and measurement of costs or benefits is uncertain.

Others argue that cost-benefit analysis can be an important and useful exercise in assessing the impacts of regulatory actions, but the resources demanded for full and rigorous cost-benefit analysis can be excessively costly and time consuming with the result that cost-benefit analysis can impede legitimate protection. Proponents of this position fear that efforts to use cost-benefit comparisons for establishing regulatory priorities will end up emphasizing only those aspects of health, safety, and environmental protection which can be easily translated to dollar terms. Such an outcome would weigh heavily against intangible or nonmonetary aspects of health, safety, and environmental protection, which is often what these types of regulations are intended to protect or enhance in the first place. In this view, the effort to make such comparisons could impede the legitimate government role of protecting and enhancing public well-being. As a practical matter, expanding the use of cost-benefit analysis would imply committing additional agency resources in research, monitoring, and analysis.

Finally, many argue that cost-benefit analysis is an incomplete tool for regulatory impact analysis, particularly with respect to non-quantitative values, and that related methods of analysis such as risk assessment and cost-effectiveness are more appropriate. Proponents of this view argue that no one opposes the use of cost- benefit in a quantitative or qualitative sense in assessing regulatory impacts in instances where it is feasible. However, there is a wide range of opinion regarding how rigorously the method should be used, given that costs and benefits in many instances are so difficult or perhaps impossible to measure, even in an approximate way. Cost-benefit analysis, despite its widespread application, is still a developing art. Much of the policy dispute is really about the rigorous use of cost-benefit analysis versus the use of other related methods of regulatory impact assessment, such as the less rigorous use of cost-benefit (based on a combination of qualitative and quantitative assessment); risk analysis or risk assessment; and cost-effectiveness.

Executive and Legislative Interest in Cost-Benefit Analysis

From the beginning of federal environmental programs, costs imposed on industry and business, state and local governments, and consumers and taxpayers have generated concern. As a tool for identifying those costs and comparing them to environmental and health improvements, cost-benefit analysis has been a subject of research and a focus of policy debates. In many respects, the development and application of cost-benefit analysis and of risk assessment have gone hand-in-hand.

President Clinton's Executive Order 12866, the most recent of several E.O.'s on analyzing regulatory costs and benefits, sets forth criteria for the application of both risk assessment and of cost-benefit analysis in preparing major regulations. In meeting its obligations under this directive, EPA has created an "EPA economy and environment program" which carries out "research and analyses of the interactions and relationships between the economy and environmental pollution control as well as other aspects of environmental economics." A key task of the office is "developing and applying improved methods to produce economic benefit information used in benefit-cost analyses of environmental programs, policies and regulations."[21]

Likewise, in the Unfunded Mandates Reform Act (P.L. 104-4), Title II, Congress requires federal agencies to quantitatively assess benefits, including the effect of a federal mandate on health, safety, and the natural environment, and to compare benefits to costs for all rules with an expected

[21] See EPA's webpage for the program [http://199.223.18.220/ee/epa/eed.nsf/pages/aboutee] and especially the hotlink to Regulatory Economic Analysis at the EPA by Robert Anderson and Paul Kobrin: [http://199.223.18.220/ee/epalib/riaepa.nsf]

cost of $100 million or more in a year. As noted in the risk assessment section above, recent Congresses have worked on legislation that would foster and in some cases require more rigorous application of cost-benefit analysis by regulatory agencies. For example, S. 746 (Levin-Thompson), the Regulatory Improvement Act of 1999 [106th Congress] would codify the requirements for cost-benefit analysis and risk assessment for major rules.

Informing Public Choices[22]

One widely used tool today is making environmentally-relevant data available to consumers, voters, corporations, and policy and program administrations so they can make environmentally-informed choices among competing products or programs. (Conceptually, there is a parallel with energy or pollution taxes, which convey price signals to consumers, corporate officials, and others.) Various public laws mandate public dissemination of information such as the environmental impacts of alternative federal programs, relative energy efficiency of products, and emissions of pollutants:

- The National Environmental Policy Act (P.L. 91-190) requires U.S. government agencies to include in every recommendation or report on proposals for legislation and other major federal actions significantly affecting the quality of the human environment, a detailed environmental impact statement.

- The Energy Policy and Conservation Act (P.L. 94-163, in Section 322), as amended by the Energy Policy Act (P.L. 102- 486, Sees. 121-126), requires that household appliances and some commercial equipment be labeled by the Federal Trade Commission with an energy efficiency rating developed by the Department of Energy to allow buyers to assess the energy consumption and potential cost savings of alternative products.

- The Energy Policy and Conservation Act (P.L. 94-163) also requires the EPA Administrator to report annually in a Fuel Economy Guide estimates for miles per gallon (mpg) rankings for

[22] Prepared by Linda-Jo Schierow, Specialist in Environmental Policy, Resources, Science, and Industry Division.

passenger vehicles to help consumers make informed choices about fuel economy when selecting new or used vehicles.

- The Emergency Planning and Community Right-to-Know Act (P.L. 99-499, Title III) mandates annual reports to the EPA by industries with pollutant emissions to the environment; after EPA compiles these reports in the Toxics Release Inventory (TRI), they are issued publically.

- The Residential Lead-Based Paint Hazard Reduction Act of 1992 (P.L. 102-550, Title X) requires the certification of contractors and laboratories engaged in detection and control of lead hazards, the publication of an "information pamphlet" on lead hazards that includes lists of certified contractors, and the disclosure of lead hazards to purchasers or lessees of targeted housing.

Criticism and Support for Information Provision

Industries targeted by information provision strategies usually are required to generate and report to government the requisite data which the governmental agency then makes available to the general public. As reporting requirements escalate, some industries have objected to the cost, not only for data gathering and reporting, but also for producing and presenting to the public other information to "provide context" for the data which otherwise may be misleading. Some businesses have been concerned about the public release of data that might reveal confidential business information and compromise economic competitiveness. In a few cases, chemical companies and other facilities that handle dangerous chemicals have argued that there are risks of terrorism that could be exacerbated if certain information were easily accessible, for example information about the potential consequences of accidents at various facilities.

Environmental and consumer advocacy groups have championed these tools. They argue that citizens have a "right to know" about potential environmental risks to which they maybe exposed, and that information approaches such as the TRI have been successful in the past in promoting more environmentally responsible corporate behavior. TRI is credited by right-to-know advocates with reducing releases of many toxic chemicals from manufacturers by more than 50%. On occasion, manufacturers also have promoted use of these tools, especially as an alternative to federal regulation of emissions or manufacturing practices.

Proponents argue that providing information works with a free economic market rather than against it, facilitates pollution prevention and creative pollution reduction strategies, and encourages stakeholder involvement in decisionmaking and enforcement. It facilitates voluntary efforts to protect the environment, and may be one of the few options for reducing pollution that is the cumulative effect of numerous daily individual decisions. On the other hand, the tool is only as good as the information; information that is inaccurate, confusing, misleading, out-of-date, irrelevant, or incomplete could distort rather than improve decisions. Similarly, there may be little benefit, or greater environmental harm could result, if the selection of reporting parameters (for example, under TRI) encourages industry to use alternative substances or processes which may pose even greater risk than the reported or regulated substance or process.

Under the Clinton Administration, EPA worked vigorously to expand public access to information, especially electronically. EPA has promised to "make 100 percent of EPA's non-confidential environmental data available and accessible to the public in a user-friendly manner" by 2003.[23]

PUBLIC SECTOR PROCESSES

Reforming the federal role in environmental protection has attracted much attention. One group of such proposals would mandate risk assessment and/or cost- benefit analysis (which have been discussed previously), with varying institutional overseers. Another related set of proposals would constrain the federal regulatory scope, for example by establishing a regulatory budget, which would be based on costs imposed. But by far the most attention to the federal role has focused on its relation to state (and local) roles.

Environmental Federalism[24]

Giving states more responsibility or a larger role in environmental management is one of the oldest new ideas in environmental policymaking and implementation. Variously termed environmental federalism,

[23] U.S. EPA, Office of the Chief Financial officer, EPA Strategic Plan [EPA/190-R-97-002/] (Washington, D.C., Sept. 1997), p. 17.

[24] Prepared by Claudia Copeland, Specialist in Resources and Environmental Policy, Resources, Science, and Industry Division.

devolution, decentralization, defederalization, or civic environmentalism-all of these terms have been used in recent years - the concept involves returning some decisionmaking authority from the federal to state and local governments. Environmental federalism, or devolution (or accountable devolution, as it has most recently been termed), is based in part on returning to intergovernmental relationships that predominated before enactment of today's federal environmental laws. In the intervening 30 years, however, both federal and state environmental programs have evolved considerably. Notably, states have enacted laws and developed management capacity to a much greater extent than was the case before 1970.

Development of the Federal Role in Environmental Policy

Regulation and management of pollution was almost entirely the province of state and local governments before the 1970s. States had virtually unlimited discretion to protect local environmental quality, yet most failed to act. During the late 1960s and early 1970s, many environmental concerns previously seen as local issues became federal issues, and the proper role of each level of government in implementing policies has been debated continuously since then. The primary impetus for the major federal environmental statutes was the perceived need for a national response to states' inaction, by providing a minimum level of environmental quality throughout the country. Historically, environmental policymakers justified a strong federal role on the basis of several considerations: (1) the implications of interstate or transboundary pollution which individual states could not effectively control; (2) fear that states competing for economic development will engage in a "race to the bottom," if left to their own devices; (3) concern that a hodgepodge of separate state regulation will impose financial costs on out-of-state producers operating in national markets; and (4) belief that administrative efficiency and economies of scale can be achieved by developing complex technical standards at the national level.

The organizing principle of federal environmental laws is that policy is developed at the national level, and programs are implemented at the state level. For 30 years, federal environmental policy was characterized by command-and-control strategies with states acting primarily through a system of delegated authority administered by EPA. Issues of day-to-day program management often strain the state-EPA relationships. There have been a number of thorny issues, which are now driving the agenda for change in intergovernmental relationships in environmental policy. The most contentious are costs (program costs and unfunded federal mandates) and federal micromanagement of states.

Current Support for Increased State Responsibility

The numerous advocates of increased state responsibility in environmental management reflect a spectrum of views on the issue. Some see the debate in terms of needing to strengthen the existing EPA-state partnership, while others argue for more complete shifting of responsibilities. On one end are those in state agencies, governors' offices, and top levels of EPA itself who believe that states should have more discretionary authority (flexibility) to implement federal laws, so that states can address their highest environmental priorities and establish resource allocations based on those priorities. Concurrently, these advocates believe that EPA should lighten the burden of oversight where states are willing to take on added responsibility. They cite several reasons for changing the EPA-state relationship and increasing state responsibility. First, the issue of state capacity to manage programs has changed. Unlike 30 years ago, states today have working environmental programs, and the federal government is not forcing states to create programs. Second, relying on traditional command-and- control methods derived from nationally uniform requirements is less effective in meeting today's changed environmental protection needs. The current generation of environmental problems (ranging from sprawl to nonpoint source pollution to watershed management and pollution impacts from people rather than companies) points to the need for state and local governments to wield the policy lever, they say, and points to the need to move beyond "one-size-fits-all" regulatory approaches established centrally.

On the other end of the spectrum of environmental federalism proponents are views represented by some academics and economists, who may bring a more ideological approach to the debate. Some argue, for example, that the command-and-control regulatory strategy that dominates environmental policy has proved inadequate, because it has not set intelligent priorities, has squandered resources, has discouraged environmentally superior technologies, and has imposed unnecessary penalties on innovation and investment. They maintain that centralized decisionmaking ignores local preferences for varying levels of environmental quality, reduces the ability of citizens to monitor government, and stifles experiments with policy options that are alternatives to one-size-fits-all. The goal of devolution, they say, is to reverse the rising power of the national government, which they see as bloated and ineffective, and to return authority to states and individuals. Some economists view these issues in terms of the implications that alternative divisions of decisionmaking responsibility have on efficiency. They are interested in questions such as which level of government might best determine the extent of environmental protection and which is most likely to select the least costly methods of control. In many cases, they believe, the answers will dictate moving the locus of decisionmaking to states and localities.

Between those who are advocating primarily an enhanced federal-state partnership and those seeking a more complete shifting of roles are other groups who support many of these arguments, including some federal legislators who advance policy and budgetary initiatives to restrict or curtail the federal role and those in industry who want less stringent federal regulation. A federal role would continue, all agree, but would be restricted to setting national standards, monitoring and enforcing compliance, providing technical assistance, and addressing transboundary pollution problems.

Policy literature on this topic has continued to grow, with reports and recommendations from a number of non-partisan or stakeholder groups (such as the National Academy of Public Administration and the National Environmental Policy Institute), as well as advocacy groups (e.g., the American Enterprise Institute, Cato Institute, and the Progressive Policy Institute). These studies have advocated and endorsed devolving existing environmental management responsibilities to capable state and local governments to tailor regulatory solutions to local problems and concerns, while leaving the federal government to address cross-boundary and international issues.

Opposition to Increased State Responsibility

While there is considerable support for environmental federalism, there is significant opposition, as well. Environmentalists, in particular, who have traditionally supported a strong federal role that provides a core level of environmental protection for all citizens and a level playing field across the country, believe that a federal programmatic baseline is an important counterbalance to potential state backsliding that could result from devolution. For these groups, concern persists that state capacity to shoulder the responsibility of devolution is less robust than state regulators say, although it is hard to either prove or disprove this assertion. Given flexibility, they say, states fail to meet high-priority program requirements, such as monitoring, permitting, and enforcement. States may set lax standards in order to lure industry or succumb to pressure by industry to adopt weak standards. Some environmentalists are concerned that states will shift away from enforcement towards compliance assistance and also reduce public involvement and participation.

Environmental Federalism Today

Devolution, or environmental federalism, is occurring today, and the basic issue is one of timing and extent. Debate continues over the degree of oversight that EPA exercises and degrees of responsibility, authority, and accountability that it gives to states. In May 1995, EPA and states took a major step towards devolution when they entered into a commitment to an improved partnership called the National Environmental Performance Partnership System (NEPPS). In it, EPA and states agreed that states should establish their own comprehensive environmental plans and identify environmental priorities. National minimum standards will remain, but EPA will allow more flexible approaches to achieve national goals. EPA oversight will focus on ensuring that states achieve environmental results, not on process. As of May 2000, 34 states have developed Performance Partnership Agreements with EPA under NEPPS.

In return for the autonomy and flexibility that states seek, all of the advocates of environmental federalism acknowledge that accountability for environmental performance is key - thus, the source of the phrase often used today to describe these developments, "accountable devolution." Accountability is necessary to address concerns of critics such as environmentalists who fear that devolution will lead to disintegration of national programs. The largest challenge for EPA and states is to build a foundation of meaningful indicators for a transformed performance-based system. The success of such a system depends on the ability to measure environmental progress in lieu of measuring traditional programmatic outputs (such as number of enforcement actions).

Chapter 5

INCENTIVES

Incentives, including both financial and technical support, predated the regulatory command and control environmental protection programs. They remained a critical complement to those programs - most notably sewage treatment grants as a complement to the water quality regulatory program. And new forms of incentives are components of various alternatives - for example, of the best management practices approach to controlling agricultural pollution (see under Management Principles below). Of various new incentives being proposed, rewarding entities that undertake environmental protection initiatives that go beyond regulatory requirements has gotten particular attention.

BEYOND COMPLIANCE: INCENTIVES FOR ENVIRONMENTAL PERFORMANCE[25]

The concept of businesses and other regulated entities achieving improved environmental performance beyond what is strictly required to meet regulatory obligations is often called "beyond compliance." Some say that, besides being overly prescriptive, the current environmental management system fails to reward excellent performers. Truly voluntary initiatives by some businesses that are intended to encourage improved environmental performance (such as environmental audits and Environmental Management Systems) attract some businesses and

---

[25] Prepared by Claudia Copeland, Specialist in Resources and Environmental Policy, Resources, Science, and Industry Division.

industries, but participation is limited. While businesses enter into such voluntary commitments for various reasons, including a perception by some that good environmental practice is good for business, the numbers that will do so without some type of incentive is likely to be small.

Recent Literature and Activity Advocating Beyond Compliance

A number of recent reports and contributions to the policy literature have examined how the United States could adopt environmental management systems using alternatives to command-and-control regulation. Some of this literature explicitly recommends that whatever new systems evolve and develop should include incentives to encourage and reward those whose environmental protection performance exceeds basic requirements. For example, the 1995 report of the National Academy of Public Administration, *Setting Priorities, Getting Results*, recommended that EPA support legislation to provide flexibility and accountability to businesses and local governments in exchange for better-than-required performance A similar theme was expressed in the 1996 report of The Aspen Institute, *Alternative Path*, which recommended that in the future the United States should utilize two parallel environmental regulatory tracks. One would be the existing system. An alternative would allow volunteers to propose pilot demonstrations of better ways to achieve environmental progress. Only projects yielding a greater net benefit than expected from existing or anticipated regulations could become pilots, but participants would receive regulatory flexibility in order to encourage their environmental protection innovations.

The concept of providing incentives to encourage beyond compliance environmental performance underlies a number of EPA's recent regulatory reinvention projects and programs. These include the ongoing Project XL, which was largely based on principles in the *Alternative Path* report and seeks to encourage up to 50 site-specific experiments to achieve better environmental outcomes along with operational flexibility and other benefits. The Common Sense Initiative (CSI), which lasted from 1994 to 1998, is related to Project XL. It sought to remove barriers to innovation by implementing multi-media projects in six specific industrial sectors. EPA's newest regulatory reinvention program, called the National Environmental Performance Track, was announced in June 2000. EPA says it is intended to reward companies which exceed minimum regulatory requirements and take extra steps to reduce and prevent pollution, including having an operational Environmental Management System. Benefits for participants will include national recognition, regulatory and administrative flexibility, a more cooperative relationship with EPA, a reduction in record keeping and reporting requirements, and flexibility in meeting certain regulatory requirements.[26] Several states (including New Jersey, Massachusetts, and Minnesota) also have adopted regulatory reinvention programs which provide qualifying facilities with flexibility under state and/or federal rules in exchange for improved environmental performance.

The types of incentives appropriate or necessary to encourage beyond compliance environmental performance are varied. They range from direct financial incentives (e.g., tax subsidies for installing pollution control equipment), to indirect financial incentives (such as more rapid permitting, less stringent standards or monitoring, more flexibility to meet standards, or less frequent renewal of permits), to public recognition in the form of a Presidential merit award or EPA certificate, to better relations with regulators, corporate customers, or non-corporate customers. The most powerful incentives are likely to be those that contribute directly or indirectly to the corporate bottom line.[27]

Support and Criticism

Proponents of providing incentives for beyond compliance performance include business and industry participants, who favor the prospect of regulatory flexibility and other benefits, and top federal and state environmental officials, who view such policies as integral to more efficient, performance-based management systems in the future. Opponents include some environmentalists who criticize policies that potentially would allow companies to sidestep regulations or obtain regulatory relief with no guarantee of environmental outcome. As with a number of other recent environmental management tools, there is a fundamental conflict between business's desire for flexibility and simplicity and environmentalists' desire for certainty and enforceability.

As a tool of environmental policy, incentives for beyond compliance are related to a number of other ideas intended to move beyond rigid regulatory strategies and towards performance-based approaches, especially use of market incentives, management practices, and devolution or defederalization. Unlike most of these other new or newer approaches, however, beyond compliance incentives lack statutory authority, a fact that

[26] In September, EPA announced that Epson Portland Inc. of Hillsboro, Oregon, is the first company accepted for the National Environmental Performance Track. (For additional information, see [http://www.epa.gov/performancetrack].)

[27] Davies, Terry, and Jan Mazurek. Industry Incentives for Environmental Improvement: Evaluation of U.S. Federal Initiatives. Global Environmental Management Initiative. Washington, 1996:7.

some proponents believe is an obstacle. These supporters argue that many companies (especially small ones) will remain reluctant to innovate because they view the transaction costs as being too high in terms of uncertain rules, consensus requirements, and unclear benefits at the end of the process. At the same time, there has been little discussion and there is no consensus on how to change statutes to address these kinds of uncertainties.

Chapter 6

MARKET MECHANISMS

Employing market mechanisms in environmental protection has been an evolving policy approach for certain types of problems since the mid-seventies. Such mechanisms have the potential to reduce the compliance costs of some environmental protection actions. These cost saving potentials are an important reason that the EPA introduced greater flexibility in implementing some Clean Air Act regulations and that Congress authorized a market-based approach to acid rain control. Such mechanisms have also been authorized in the international treaty dealing with possible future actions to slow global climate change.

This gradual development of supplements to the "command and control" regulatory approach in practice has also has been preceded and accompanied by a growing body of academic and policy community attention. Proponents of market- based approaches include think tanks, academics, and some leading environmental advocacy groups. They argue that properly structured incentive mechanisms can produce significant reduction in pollution control costs while achieving agreed upon environmental standards.

POLLUTION TRADING AND POLLUTION TAXES[28]

Market-based mechanisms fall into two distinct groups with many variations in each category. The first are trading mechanisms which allow businesses to meet a facility, regional, industry-wide, or a national cap on a pollutant by shifting their individual compliance obligations within their

[28] Prepared by John L. Moore, Assistant Director, Resources, Science and Industry Division

business operations or to other businesses subject to the same compliance requirements. For the case of trading between companies, this mechanism operates when companies with low compliance costs control their pollution beyond what is required by regulation and then sell the excess compliance to companies with high control costs. The latter companies are thus relieved of some of their pollution control obligations, avoiding costly abatement expenditures. The net effect is to concentrate compliance at the points of lowest cost, thus reducing overall compliance costs. Environmental protection is achieved in a more economically efficient manner.

A second market mechanism is the explicit taxation of a polluting activity in order to include in the cost of a good or service the social costs (environmental or human health damage) that the polluting activity may cause. By raising the cost of polluting inputs or outputs for businesses or raising the cost for consumers using polluting substances (e.g.; gasoline combustion), businesses or consumers have an incentive to economize on the polluting activity. Businesses or consumers can respond as they choose, with some paying the higher costs and others making changes that avoid the effects of the tax. The combined responses to the cost incentive in.. theory will result in a reduction in the polluting activity to a point where further reductions by businesses or consumers would cost more than paying the tax or be inconvenient or impractical. The potential reduction in pollution depends on the level of the tax. This is set, in theory, based on what is needed to meet a targeted reduction in pollution. Alternately, the tax can be set to achieve a given level of reduction in the incremental monetized damages caused by the pollutant. This assumes that complex environmental and human health values and attributes can be translated to monetary surrogates. Although widely advocated by economists, this incentive mechanism has never been employed in U.S. environmental laws or regulations except as fees or charges intended to raise revenue or cover regulatory administrative costs. Such charges typically are low enough not to create incentive effects for reducing pollution levels.

Both trading mechanisms and pollution taxes have defined circumstances in which they have been or could be effective in environmental management.

For trading mechanisms, like sulfur allowance trading for acid rain control or the EPA's netting, banking, and offset programs for some criteria air pollutants, several business and institutional circumstances are necessary for effective implementation. These programs are likely to be effective when: 1) the pollutant is one where transactions and information costs are low, typically when industries have long experience with monitoring and controlling a pollutant, there are a large but fairly set number of possible market participants, and there are intermediary institutions to facilitate trading; 2) security of long term investments in pollution control by companies is highly certain, so that unanticipated future changes do not impede long term planning and financial commitments; 3) there are several technically and financially feasible options for reducing pollution among different industry segments (fuel switching, process changes, etc.); and 4) reductions are sought across a broad geographical area for a pollutant that does not involve local public health or environmental effects or alternately within one jurisdiction or facility, so that third party impacts are minimized. Thus, the advantages of trading mechanisms are their potential for lower-cost implementation of environmental controls in situations where a set number of large sources can potentially optimize expenditures on abatement through mutually beneficial exchange of the location of control. On the other hand, for pollution from diffuse and numerous sources, trading mechanisms do not appear very practical given the high transaction and information costs needed for implementation.

Taxation as a tool for reducing environmental damage is particularly applicable to problems where pollution is the result of small, diffuse, and numerous sources. In these cases, meeting environmental objectives requires an overall reduction in the total consumption or use of a polluting material or activity, but the large number of contributors makes traditional regulation or targeted reductions difficult. With population, GDP, material consumption, and waste flows all growing, mitigating environmental deterioration may be extremely difficult or impossible to manage without the use of incentives. Some forms of air and water pollution, 002 generation, and traffic congestion are examples where taxation or other price signals could be a relevant management tool. Taxes on polluting substances and activities send a signal to consumers and businesses to make short and long term alterations, without prescribing how or what to modify. The advantages of using this tool are its administrative simplicity; the flexibility it gives those affected to respond; and its long term effects on innovation and technical and behavioral changes.

While the theory and logic for using taxes to reduce certain types of environmental deterioration are straightforward, this approach meets public as well as policy objections on several fronts. First, those who would pay such taxes may oppose this approach as being unfair if other types of pollution sources are not being taxed, and as diverting monies that could be used for pollution abatement investments. Second, if large sums of money are involved, how such revenue is used is a critical question (some argue for use in environmental programs or recycling through income tax relief, but questions of tax base stability arise). Third, agreeing on the appropriate level of a pollution tax is problematic due to uncertainty about the exact reductions in pollution that may result. Finally, questions of pollution taxes become involved in broader tax policy issues which complicate practical implementation.

PRIVATE MARKETS AND LEGAL ACTIONS[29]

Under some circumstances, environmental protection can be achieved between private parties without direct statutory and regulatory involvement. Some argue that these tools if used more extensively could avoid the inefficiencies of bureaucratic regulation, although critics contend that the circumstances are more narrowly delimited than proponents acknowledge. In one case, if pollution rights are clearly defined between two parties where one is generating pollution, bargaining can lead to an economically efficient reduction in the pollution level. In a second case, tort actions based on injuries suffered due to pollution can result in court rulings that restrict defendants or compensate plaintiffs; and polluters will consider the benefits of reducing the threat of liability in accounting for costs of pollution reduction. Finally, in a third situation, private property rights can be used to protect resources vulnerable to the "tragedy of the commons" (in which common ownership leads to overexploitation as each participant seeks to maximize gain).

Markets in Pollution Rights

In the case of bargaining between private parties, the potential for finding an economically efficient reduction exists when a clearly traceable pollution source operated by one party is causing verifiable damages or loss to another party. Under specific and site-dependent circumstances, such private transactions can produce economically efficient environmental protection.

If the right to discharge pollution is clearly defined or alternately, the right to be free of pollution is clearly defined, negotiations between the parties can lead to an efficient balance between reducing pollution damages

[29] Prepared by John L. Moore, Assistant Director, Resources, Science and Industry Division.

and expenditures to reduce pollution. This occurs because either party has an incentive to bargain with the other. In the case where the polluter has the rights to discharge wastes, the negatively affected party can offer to pay the polluter to reduce discharges to the point that the monetary value of remaining damages is below the cost of additional abatement expenditures to the polluting party. On the other hand, if the party that potentially would be damaged has the right to be free of pollution, the party that needs to pollute in order to operate can negotiate a level of compensation in order to find a balance between abatement expenditures and purchasing from the other party the right to discharge some pollution. Depending on equality in bargaining positions, an "optimal" reduction in pollution would result. Which party draws the greater benefit from the exchange depends on who holds the initial pollution rights. This type of situation is an example of what is called the Coase theorem (after a classic article by Professor Ronald Coase) in which a clear assignment of property rights in theory will lead to an economically efficient reduction in pollution through private party bargaining. This outcome, however, rests on the assumption of no barriers to transactions such as imperfect knowledge, limited rationality, or communications costs. It assumes equality of bargaining positions, clear and provable linkages between polluter and the injured party, minimal transaction costs (meaning, generally a limited number of parties), and the absence of potential free riders on the agreements reached between the bargaining parties.

Private Legal Remedies

In the second case, where pollution rights are ill- defined, or custom has implicitly assumed that pollution is accepted as part of economic activity, legal remedies sometimes can lead to a balance between pollution reduction costs on the one hand and avoided injuries to other parties on the other. A variety of legal theories may be available to plaintiffs such as nuisance, negligence, trespass, infliction of mental distress, and strict liability. For example, under the common law doctrine of nuisance, as well as under other legal theories, courts can award compensation of injuries or injunctions to parties injured by pollution. In situations where there is one polluter and the nature of hardships favors the plaintiffs, nuisance remedies can be an effective management tool. This assumes that plaintiff has the money, time, and patience to see the action through. Class actions also help. As a hypothetical example, if air emissions from a factory were causing damage to crops on downwind farms, the farmers could seek an injunction and compensatory damages for any losses in the value of their crops. A court could find any number of ways to address the situation depending on the severity of damages to the crops and the economic consequences of enjoining further pollution from the factory. For example, if the plant was the mainstay of the local economy and had already undertaken extensive pollution abatement expenditures and the aggregate damages to crops were small, a court could find against enjoining the factory from further pollution. In this type of situation, some state courts have chosen to "balance the equities" and deny injunctions since the resulting hardships to the defendant outweigh the harm to the plaintiffs. However, where injunctions are denied, sometimes courts have awarded past or ongoing compensatory damages to plaintiffs.

In general, nuisance law has had only limited effectiveness in controlling wide- spread pollution. In addition to the tendency to balance the equities and deny injunctions, other factors have limited nuisance law as an effective tool in controlling widespread pollution. One important limitation is the lack of eligibility to sue. The common law distinguishes between private and public nuisances, where the latter may involve small damages to large numbers of people. In cases of public nuisances, in general, only a state attorney general or a local prosecutor has been allowed to bring a law suit against polluters. Reluctance by governments to bring suits that would harm local industries has mostly limited the role of injunctive relief, though some states now allow individuals to bring suits to mitigate public nuisances.

Another complication that has limited the usefulness of nuisance remedies is the burden of proof on the plaintiffs. Widespread pollution typically comes from many sources, none of which alone could be shown to produce the resulting injury. It is further difficult to achieve a group of defendants among whom potential damages can be allocated. In general, then, common law remedies under nuisance law do not provide a sufficiently systematic means for managing widespread pollution discharges to environmental media. In other types of legal actions, similar issues of causation and accountability limit such methods for dealing with widespread pollution which is typical of must contemporary environmental problems.

Environmental Markets

In a third situation, creating markets for transactions of environmental "goods," may lead to efficient outcomes. (In pollution control, trading programs, as discussed above, constitute a type of environmental market). In some cases, private parties may act through existing markets to achieve environmental protection ends, as for example when the Nature Conservancy buys private land in order to protect it and its resources, or when a private landowner sells hunting or fishing rights (and thereby has a vested interest in maintaining healthy populations of the sport game or fish). In other cases, governmental intervention may be needed to create the market for an environmental good or service, as for example when governmental bodies allow the selling of development rights as a way of channeling development from environmental sensitive areas to less sensitive areas, or when state and federal governments provide for market transactions of water rights.

Market approaches are being actively debated for allocating water resources[30] and certain fisheries.[31] Proponents of what is sometimes called "envirocapitalism" have cataloged numerous other examples that demonstrate the potential power of environmental markets. Examples include the Fossil Rim Wildlife Center in Texas, the marketing of paddlefish roe in Montana, the retirement of salmon quotas by the North Atlantic Salmon Fund, and wildlife management in Zimbabwe.[32]

How to generalize from the anecdotal successes of environmental markets (and from failures of common ownership of resources) is not easy, however. A key issue is the original endowment of rights: first-in-time, first-in-right effectively legitimizes historical patterns of income and property; while changing those rights raises questions of due process. For example, should fishing rights be vested to those now fishing, or should those rights be auctioned to give every one an opportunity of entry? (In the case of sulfur oxides emission allowances,[33] existing facilities received allowances based on historical emissions, and new sources have to buy into the limited number of allowances available.) A second key issue arises from the complex interactions that can be affected by transactions in environmental markets. Promoting markets for resources such as game animals and fish may have divergent impacts on broader ecosystems and other community and public values - for example, on nongame species, helping some and harming others, or on other resources, such as water use.

---

[30] Terry L. Anderson and Peter J. Hill, eds.. Water Marketing-The Next Generation (Lanham, MD: Rowman and Littlefield Publishers, Inc., 1997; and Richard W. Wahl, Markets/or Federal Water: Subsidies, Property Rights, and the Bureau of Reclamation (Washington, D.C.: Resources for the Future, 1989).

[31] Eugene H. Buck, Individual Quotas in Fishery Management, CRS Report 95-849 ENR.

[32] See Terry L. Anderson and Donald R. Leal, Enviro-Capitalists: Doing Good While Doing Well (Lanham, Md. : Rowman & Littlefield Publishers, 1997).

[33] The Clean Air Act specifies that the allowances do not constitute "property rights" (§403(0); hence they could be revoked without penalty.

As with so many of the other alternatives to command and control regulation, the creation of environmental markets is an evolving tool. It includes not just markets in goods and services, but also in qualities, over time, as with the sale and transference of development rights. While these initiatives can bring the power of the market to bear on environmental goods, they may require governmental structuring of the markets and defining of the transactions.

Chapter 7

MANAGEMENT PRINCIPLES

Addressing environmental protection as a problem of changing decisionmakers' values underlies a set of approaches that may be called "management principles." These approaches focus on the way managers make decisions with environmental consequences. The managers involved can include not only corporate managers, but also managers of public lands and resources, individual property owners, and, in some cases, regulatory officials as well.

The "command-and-control" regulatory system specifies what is to be done or accomplished; enhancing information and "market-based" systems presume environmentally protective decisions will follow from neutral competence and/or self- interested responses to the information or the price and cost signals. In contrast, the management principles approaches seek to achieve environmental protection goals by redirecting managers' criteria for making decisions affecting the environment. New information, changed cost/price signals, incentives, even regulatory standards maybe involved; but the key elements of management principles approaches involve, first, inculcating a heightened awareness of environmental protection needs in managers, and second, providing some criterion or yardstick for decisionmakers to assess the environmental implications of choices. If a manager can accurately anticipate the consequences of decisions and has accepted environmental values, environmentally preferable choices should follow voluntarily - a crucial difference from regulation.

Management principles approaches themselves range from the relatively abstract, such as "sustainability," to the pragmatic, such as "best management practices" for agricultural tillage and environmental "audits."

SUSTAINABILITY - SUSTAINABLE DEVELOPMENT[34]

The term sustainable development emerged in its current form in 1987 in the final report of the United Nations World Commission on Environment and Development (WCED), known as the Brundtland Commission after its chairman, then Norwegian Prime Minister Gro Harlem Brundtland. The definition most widely quoted in the WCED report is: "Development that meets the needs of the present without compromising the ability of future generations to meet their own needs."

In the more detailed treatment of the term, the report identified requirements for sustainability to include citizen participation in the political system, a self-reliant and sustained economic system, a social system that allows for solutions for tensions from "disharmonious development," a production system that respects the ecological base, a technological system that continuously searches for new solutions, an administrative system that is flexible and has the capacity for self-correction, and an international system that fosters sustainable patterns of trade and finance.

Summing up these components, the WCED report stated, "In its broadest sense, the strategy for sustainable development aims to promote harmony among human beings and between humanity and nature." Popular usage has made sustainable development nearly synonymous in many circles with "environmentally compatible development." In 1992, following up on the Brundtland Commission report, the United Nations Conference on Environment and Development (UNCED, popularly known as the Earth Summit) was held in Rio de Janeiro. The Conference produced the Rio Declaration on Environment and Development, plus a 40-chapter action plan called "Agenda 21" (referring to the 21st Century). Agenda 21 posits sustainable development as key to most areas of development, and discusses both what individual nations should undertake to achieve it and what the international community should do. The Rio Declaration endorses actions such as environmental impact assessment, public participation, effective environmental legislation, cooperation to promote an open international economic system, and the precautionary approach (this last is discussed in a following section). One of the most general principles, number 25, states, "Peace, development and environmental protection are interdependent and indivisible."

---

[34] Prepared by Susan R. Fletcher, Senior Analyst in International Environmental Policy, Resources, Science and Industry Division.

At a practical level, sustainable development is a planning and decision framework. For example, optimal management of a fishery or of lumbering of a forest can be based on the criterion of sustainability, in which, as a first principle, harvesting only the annual growth from a fish or timber stock assures a perpetual yield from the resource base. In other words, society consumes only the interest from its asset, not the principal itself. At a broader level, sustainable development involves both an understanding and a commitment (by individuals, businesses, communities, and various levels of government) to set and meet goals or constraints on key determinants of the ecological or environmental health of an environmental system. The goals or constraints represent indicators or variables which must be maintained at certain levels if the system in the long term is to yield desired human uses and benefits without degrading or seriously damaging the system. The goals or constraints set the context for decision makers to use various economic and regulatory tools, such as tradable permits, taxation of pollution, best management practices, cost-effectiveness, risk assessment, or cost-benefit analysis.

The local, interstate, and federal efforts to improve the ecology of the Chesapeake Bay can be viewed in the sustainability framework. Science and research have determined that, in order to enhance the fishery and recreational values of the Bay and ensure their sustainability into the future, dissolved oxygen levels and water clarity must improve from current levels and harvest levels on commercial and recreational species must be established and enforced. To achieve those goals, nutrient and sediment loadings must be reduced. To do that, a host of watershed- wide land use management practices (buffering tributaries with forest-cover, protecting and expanding wetlands, improving urban storm water management, limiting agricultural runoff, etc.) and a similar host of direct pollution control improvements (upgraded sewage and industrial waste water treatment, reduced nitrogen oxide emissions from transportation and industry sources, improved septic system performance, etc.) must be undertaken. Achieving such improvements, then, is a process of applying a range of tools (informational, economic, and regulatory) within numerous government and citizen planning and decision making processes. The ultimate measure of success would be the long-term viability of the Bay's resources.

In practice, the application of the sustainability concept to environmental program management is proceeding along several lines, notably: (1) within the economic discipline, evaluating what it means with respect to economic concepts of growth, development, and social welfare; (2) within executive and ministerial bodies, assessing what it means for environmental planning and management; and (3) within specific programs, focusing on what it means for accomplishing "on the ground" practices.

The Economics of Sustainability

At present, "sustainability" remains on the periphery of economic practice; however, a number of economic theoreticians have been exploring how to incorporate the insight behind the concept into economic theory and understanding.[35] So-called "green accounting" is the idea of modifying national accounts, such as Gross Domestic Product, so that resource depreciation is incorporated. However, efforts to develop "national indicators of progress toward sustainable progress" have been controversial and in the United States they have yet to be widely endorsed or to be formally adopted.[36]

Planning[37]

In the eight years since UNCED, the U.N. Commission on Sustainable Development (CSD) has met annually at the United Nations to review what countries are doing to implement the elements of Agenda 21. National reports submitted to the CSD detail what countries are doing in various focus areas such as pollution control, forestry, water resources, agriculture, etc. In many, if not most, cases it is difficult to sort out which, if any, actions proceed with conscious reference to Agenda 21 or to sustainable development as an organizing principle. In some developing countries, such as China, action plans around principles of Agenda 21 have been identified.

However, the concept of sustainability has been adopted and integrated into the terminology of development in a number of European government efforts,[38] and in the United States there has been extensive activity -

---

[35] E.g., "Processes for Environmental Valuation: Procedures and Institutions for Social Valuations of Natural Capitals in Environmental Conservation and Sustainability Policy." See: [http://alba.jrc.it/valse/noappletvalse.htm]

[36] See Organization for Economic Co-operation and Development, Towards Sustainable Development: Indicators to Measure Progress (OECD, 2000), especially pp. 194-197, on the experience of the United States. See also, [http://www.sdi.gov]

[37] The World Wide Web Virtual Library "SUSTAINABLE DEVELOPMENT" gives access to a broad range of activities, at [http://www.ulb.ac.be/ceese/meta/sustvl.html]; see also the "sustainable development gateway" on the web: [http://sdgateway.net/default.htm]

[38] The concept was added to the European Union constitution in 1997 and by July 2001 the European Commission is expected to introduce a "sustainability strategy" to direct policies

particularly at the state and local level - around this term. In 1993, the President established the President's Council on Sustainable Development (PCSD), bringing together high-level participants from government (Cabinet secretaries), business and industry (at the CEO level), and non-governmental and academic entities, usually the heads of these organizations. The Council formed Task Forces, held extensive hearings and public meetings, and prepared numerous reports on topics such as eco-efficiency, population and consumption, energy and transportation, sustainable agriculture, etc. The Council submitted a report Sustainable America: A New Consensus in 1996, having adopted the Brundtland Commission definition. It outlined a vision statement that "articulates the Council's broad concept of the benefits of sustainability to the Nation." The Council outlined 10 broad goals, such as ensuring a healthy and clean environment, economic prosperity, equity, conservation of nature, civic engagement, population stabilization, education, and sustainable communities. It published a second report Towards a Sustainable America in 1999. It included chapters on Climate Change, Environmental Management, Metropolitan and Rural Strategies, and International Leadership, with each chapter including recommendations for concrete actions. Since the appearance of this report, it is unclear whether a federal entity charged with a comprehensive sustainability mandate will be continued, although some federal agencies have incorporated this concept into their policy framework.

Practical Applications

At the local level, a Joint Clearinghouse on Sustainable Communities was established by the National Association of Counties and the National Conference of Mayors in 1996 at the request of President Clinton, in which the quite extensive array of activities undertaken by communities, towns, cities and states in the United States are tracked. In most cases, these efforts begin with a decision by a town, county or state government to commit to sustainable development, followed by the convening of multi-stakeholder councils, commissions, or committees to decide on the process to be used. The dialog that follows usually attempts to identify key goals of the community, then arrive at recommended actions to achieve sustainability as those goals are conceived. The key concept underlying these attempts is that sustainability can be achieved only if the trade-offs between potentially

of governmental sectors. See [http://europa.eu.int/comm/environment/forum/governance_en.pdf.]

conflicting goals are identified early in the process, and mechanisms devised to assure that one stakeholder's goals are not undermined as other stakeholders' goals are achieved. Participants in this dialog often feel that they have had a beneficial learning experience when unrecognized trade-offs are brought to their attention. But arriving at a means of achieving all stakeholders' goals usually requires some compromises. As these compromises are identified and debated, the sustainable development effort often becomes a very painful process, and it often breaks down without arriving at action points.

Overall, the effort to define and achieve sustainability has involved a significant amount of consciousness raising about the trade-offs involved in community decision- making, especially those such as environmental ones, which economic development activities often tend to ignore. At its best, it is a process for ensuring that otherwise overlooked perspectives and constituencies are not excluded from decisions. But it remains an ill-defined process in which operational results remain elusive.

PRECAUTIONARY PRINCIPLE[39]

How managers should assess potential hazards has been debated for many years. It was a key issue in the debates over the Toxic Substances Control Act, enacted in 1976. Its resolution of the issue was that chemical producers should be responsible for research to assess hazards, but that there had to be some trigger of concern before EPA could require such research. In recent years, the European Community has taken the lead in applying what is called the "precautionary principle." It provides a framework for making decisions in the face of uncertainty - described by one observer as a shift in environmental policy from "*react-and-cure to anticipate-and-prevent*."[40] It has also become prominent in international agreements. The 1992 Rio *Declaration on Environment and Development*, Principle 15, stated:

> In order to protect the environment, the precautionary approach shall be widely applied by States according to their capabilities. Where there are threats of serious or irreversible damage, lack of full scientific certainty

[39] Prepared by Michael Simpson, Specialist in Life Sciences, and John E. Blodgett, Deputy Assistant Director, Resources, Science, and Industry Division.

[40] A. Stewart, "Scientific Uncertainty, Ecologically Sustainable Development and the Precautionary Principle," Griffith Law Review, Vol. 8, no. 2 (1999), 364.

shall not be used as a reason for postponing cost-effective measures to prevent environmental degradation.[41]

In January 1998, an international group of scientists, government officials, attorneys, and. labor and environmental activists developed the Wingspread Statement on the Precautionary Principle which says, in part, "when an activity raises threats of harm to human health or the environment, precautionary measures should be taken even if some cause and effect relationships are not fully established scientifically. In this context the proponent of an activity, rather than the public, should bear the burden of proof."[42] The precautionary principle or approach has become a basis for European environmental law and, increasingly, European environmental health policies, as well; but in the U.S., the principle is at most implicit in environmental statutes.

The precautionary principle is not without its critics. Key objections include its variability in interpretation, its potential role in trade protectionism, and its potential to hinder the development and application of new technologies. The title of a June 1999 Harvard Center for Risk Analysis workshop on "The Precautionary Principle: Refine It or Replace It"[43] conveys the concern over how to interpret the principle. Controversies over bioengineered foods have been cited as exemplifying both trade distortions and hindrances to beneficial research and development.[44]

ECOSYSTEM MANAGEMENT[45]

Ecosystem management is an approach to land and resource management that has been conceptualized m various ways.[46] The scientific

[41] The United Nations Conference on Environmental Development, Rio de Janeiro 1992, Earth Summit '92 (London: The Regency Press Corp.,1992), p. 13.

[42] P. Montague "The Precautionary Principle," Rachel's Environment and Health Weekly, 586 (February 19, 1998), 2. http://www.monitor.net/rachel/r586.html

[43] For a brief summary, see Harvard Center for Risk Analysis, "Making Sense of the Precautionary Principle," Risk in Perspective, Vol. 7, issue 6 (Sept. 1999).

[44] See Jonathan Adler, "More Sorry Than Safe: Assessing the Precautionary Principle and the Proposed International Biosafety Protocol," Texas international Law Journal, Vol. 35, no. 173 (1999-2000), 196; and Kenneth Foster, et al., "Science and the Precautionary Principle," Science, Vol. 288 (May 12, 2000), 979-981.

[45] Prepared by Ross Gorte, Specialist in Natural Resources Policy, Resources, Science, and Industry Division.

[46] For a more detailed discussion of this issue, see U.S. Senate, Committee on Environment and Public Works, Ecosystem Management: Status and Potential. Summary of a Workshop Convened by the Congressional Research Service, March 24 and 25, 1994, S.Prt. 103-98 (Washington, DC: U.S. Govt. Print. Off., 1994), 331 p.

community has viewed ecosystem management largely as identifying environmental conditions before European settlement of North America, and examining how subsequent activities and management have altered ecosystems from these conditions. The environmental community has seen ecosystem management as using the scientific information on pre-settlement conditions to set management goals for restoring or preserving ecological processes and biological diversity. The federal land and resource management agencies have adopted ecosystem management to improve their planning processes, both expanding the geographic and ecological scope under consideration and broadening the participation of stakeholders.[47] The USDA Forest Service has recently revised its planning regulations to include "ecological sustainability" as a way to implement ecosystem management.[48]

Ecosystem management is one of several approaches that attempt to expand the historic, geographic, ecological, and participatory aspects of land and resource management. Other efforts, some of which have existed far longer than ecosystem management, include watershed management, landscape management, and multiple- use management. These approaches are all generally similar in attempting to consider interactions among uses on lands and resources, typically on broader geographic scales and over longer time periods than traditional management. They differ primarily in their geographic basis (ecosystems, watersheds, landscapes, or politically- defined management units) and their emphasis (ecological conditions; water supply and quality concerns; ecological interactions; and land and resource uses).

Background

Policies to manage resources based on an understanding of the broad environmental and social consequences of decisions have existed for decades. Multiple-use management for the national forests, for example, has been required by law since 1960, and arguably was the intent in the original 1897 forest management authority. Watershed management can be traced easily to the Water Resources Council and river basin commissions authorized in 1965. Ecosystem management appears to have been first used in Professor Eugene Odum's *Fundamentals of Ecology* in 1971, and arguably is the vision presented by Aldo Leopold in *A Sand County Almanac* in 1949.

---

[47] For a list of federal agencies with some land and/or resource management responsibilities that are implementing ecosystem management, see CRS Report 94-339 ENR, Ecosystem Management: Federal Agency Activities.

[48] 65 Federal Register 67514-67581 (Nov. 9, 2000).

Ecosystem management, as adopted by the federal agencies, can be traced to the United Nations Conference on Environment and Development (UNCED) held in June 1992 in Rio de Janeiro, Brazil. The 1989 U.N. General Assembly resolution initiating UNCED cited concerns about freshwater quality and supplies, deforestation and desertification, biological diversity, and many other' issues. UNCED included discussions of the Rio Declaration (principles on environmentally sustainable development), adopted Agenda 21 (an action program to implement the principles), and opened for signature two treaties — a convention on climate change and a convention on biological diversity. Ecosystem management for U.S. federal land and resource management agencies was an approach announced by the Bush Administration to precede the President's attendance at the Earth Summit.

Pro/Con Analysis

The various views of ecosystem management have both support and opposition. The scientific community view of ecosystem management, involving expanded historic, geographic, and ecological information, is seen as leading to better informed decisions by providing a baseline for assessing the results, especially cumulative impacts, of management efforts. However, some argue that the sciences have not progressed sufficiently to develop such information and that the cost of such data collection exceeds any improvement in decisions. There is also some concern that additional information on the conditions and uses of private lands could be used to regulate those lands, constraining the private landowners.

The environmental community views of ecosystem management largely as a goal of preserving or restoring biological diversity and ecological processes. Proponents often assert that, because it is generated by scientific research, the information is a "science-based" goal for land and resource management. They also sometimes argue that the improved information and a goal of "naturalness" for federal lands can clarify the role of the federal government, as a provider of public goods and social values, and private landowners as producers of private goods. Opponents argue that a goal of "naturalness" is unlikely to be limited to federal lands, and is likely to be used to restrict private land uses. They also argue that, while recreating historically natural conditions might be desirable for providing certain environmental values and processes, but is only one of many possible options for land and resource management.

The federal adoption of ecosystem management has been as an expansion of the planning process. Part of this expanded planning is developing broader historic and geographic information. The Forest Service and the Bureau of Land Management have conducted "ecoregional" assessments at relatively broad geographic scales that include private land conditions and uses. These agencies contend that greater information at expanded scales could lead to a better sense of the possible cumulative impacts of federal decisions, while private land information might provide a clearer understanding of the appropriate role of federal lands within a specific region. Some oppose such data development, however, as a costly exercise with few real benefits. Also, private landowners are concerned about possible regulation of their lands based on information allegedly collected to improve federal land management planning. Environmental interests criticize the federal agencies view of ecosystem management only as a planning process rather than as a goal of restoring natural conditions. This criticism might be alleviated somewhat by the November 2000 Forest Service final revised planning regulations that establish ecological sustainability as a management goal for the national forests. However, this new management goal engendered criticism of the draft regulations from groups whose uses or interests may conflict with this goal.[49] Further, some have suggested that this goal differs fundamentally from the direction in the laws currently governing national forest management, and question whether the current laws permit ecosystem management for the federal lands.[50]

Federal ecosystem management planning is, according to the agencies, also intended to promote greater cooperation in federal decisionmaking through expanded public participation. Collaboration might reduce local antipathy towards federal land ownership and produce a broader, more balanced local and regional economic base. However, the expanded planning process likely will increase the time and cost of planning, both directly by the federal government and indirectly by the public participants, especially if another planning level (ecoregional assessments) is added. The process also could exacerbate current feelings of frustration with federal land ownership if the participants do not feel that the process has been truly collaborative and led to consensus.

[49] 65 Federal Register 67514-67581 (Nov. 9, 2000).

[50] Roger A. Sedjo, "A View of the Report of the Committee of Scientists," Sustaining the People's Lands: Recommendations for Stewardship of the National Forests and Grasslands into the Next Century, by the Committee of Scientists, K. Norman Johnson, Chair (Washington, DC: March 15, 1999), p. 183.

GOOD MANAGEMENT PRACTICES[51]

Good management practices at the individual level are the least intrusive and least consistent end of the environmental policy spectrum because they rely on the good intentions of individuals. These practices encompass stewardship by landowners and leaseholders as they manage private working lands that provide diverse benefits, ranging from producing commodities such as trees and row crops to providing habitat and amenities. The most familiar applications of good management practices occur in the context of resource management activities. However, the essential concept of these practices is that good stewardship of the land - keeping soil on the land, rather than permitting it to erode into nearby streams - will benefit both the land resource and environmental quality. Good management practices are a collage of many possible actions that involve physical modifications to the landscape and sound resource management activities that provide environmental benefits. While the practices usually have a single environmental focus, such as improved water quality, they typically provide multiple benefits. These practices often are voluntarily applied, although that is not a prerequisite.

The typical role of the federal government is to provide incentives that encourage participation: (1) public cost sharing funds to help pay for planning, installation, and maintenance; (2) education to explain both their benefits and how to properly use and maintain them; and (3) technical assistance to help design and implement stewardship activities. A cornerstone is planning to assemble the most appropriate mix of practices that will help the land user reach his goals while recognizing the physical characteristics and limitations of each site and its resources. The focus of application has been on the most modified lands, which are usually lands cultivated to produce crops, but also include forest lands, range, and pasture, and at the scale of an individual ownership.

Underlying Concepts

Good management practices are designed to maintain, restore, or enhance the health and integrity of the resource base - soils, water and air, and the plants and animals that depend on them - by using tools that range

---

[51] Prepared by Jeffrey Zinn, Specialist in Natural Resources Policy, Resources, Science, and Industry Division.

from active to passive and from construction to resource management. Individual practices have design and other standards, but they vary widely in what they actually accomplish because of the dynamic nature of land uses and conditions, and users' goals. The unstated assumption is that resources benefit from these practices, not that they should benefit at least to some prescribed level, or standard.

Pros and Cons

Supporters cite many aspects of good management practices as the basis for continued and expanded use. Participation is incentive-driven, involves willing participants, and attracts those who want to improve their resources. Participation is driven by personal goals about resource protection and improvement rather than externally-generated requirements. Good management can be practiced at many different scales and levels of intensity. Practices have design standards that must be met. Each benefits the resources to different degrees, but all are improvements over the status quo for resource conditions. Land users can change their mix of good management practices; this flexibility recognizes the dynamic ways in which land users may modify their goals from year to year.

Reliance on good management practices has also been criticized. Resource problems are not evenly distributed across the landscape, so the relative interest in applying them does not match the distribution pattern of environmental problems. The result is a hodge-podge of practices that inefficiently address resource problems. In addressing the resource problems of a given area, such as a watershed, there is greater benefit when all landowners participate and when all utilize consistent practices. Also, since participation is voluntary, there are few mechanisms to insure that the practices are properly maintained after they are installed, even when federal funds help pay for the installation. Few of these programs have penalties, such as requiring the repayment of public funds if the practices are not maintained; the installation of practices is often publicized, but the ephemeral characteristics are not discussed. Further, there are few incentives for public agencies to monitor the condition or performance of these practices after they are in place, and in many cases, there are no penalties for land operators who decide not to maintain these practices.

Historical Beginnings

Good management practices can be traced back to defining events or periods. For agricultural land uses, the defining event for soil was the Dust Bowl of the 1930s, when dust storms from the Midwest blanketed that region and the West. The response was development of conservation practices that would allow crop production while reducing soil erosion. For forests, there was a defining period late in the 19th century rather than an event, with the recognition that much of the forests were disappearing, especially in the East and upper Midwest. The response was the establishment of the National Forest System and the beginnings of efforts to develop sound forest management practices.

One part of the institutional structure that supports these practices, the land grant college system, is far older, having been created in the 1860s. Because this system was already well-established when these defining events occurred, the public policy responses have drawn from this structure. The land grant college system has provided a major research component to develop new practices and improve existing ones, and also a major educational component through the USDA Extension Service.

Since the broad needs to protect and improve natural resources on private lands were first recognized, both the number of concerns and the tools to address them have expanded. Newer concerns are often more precise modifications of more general ones raised earlier. Newer tools include tillage practices, forest management techniques, and grass and rangeland management techniques. Emerging technologies, such as biotech and Geographic Information Systems, are creating new opportunities for good management practices. Recently, interest has grown in considering resource needs from a systems perspective that combines many of these factors on a scale that is larger than single land holdings, and emphasizes interrelationships among resources that resource management experts view as critical to maintaining healthy resources in the broader landscape.

Concluding Thoughts

The voluntary approach to managing these resources has generated considerable debate about their effectiveness. The voluntary approach is viewed by some as getting the strongest commitment to installing and maintaining practices because all the participants are willingly involved and have a strong desire for success. Others see limitations in this approach in that the greatest needs or worst problems are not necessarily controlled by willing land owners. They view this approach as being less efficient, both in terms of committing public resources and in terms of results. They also may view it as less enduring, as there are few features built into these programs to insure that environmental benefits are maintained. One aspect of this debate has been the questions of whether resources to conduct these programs should be distributed more-or-less equally over the landscape and be available in small amounts to many participants, as had been the case until recently, or should they be concentrated to address the worst problems or greatest needs, based on some measure of physical conditions, and the role that new technologies might play in making this approach more effective.

Pollution Prevention/ Materials Management[52]

Since passage of the Pollution Prevention Act (Title VI of the Omnibus Budget Reconciliation Act of 1990, P.L. 101-508), the Environmental Protection Agency has been required to develop and coordinate a pollution prevention strategy, and owners and operators of many industrial facilities have been required to report annually on source reduction and recycling activities as part of their submissions under the Toxics Release Inventory.

Enactment of the Pollution Prevention Act marked a turning point in the direction of U.S. environmental protection policy. From an earlier focus on the need to reduce or repair environmental damage by controlling pollutants at the point where they are released to the environment - i.e., at the "end of the pipe" or smokestack, or after disposal - Congress turned to pollution prevention through reduced generation of pollutants at their point of origin. Broad support for this policy change was based on the notion that traditional approaches to pollution control had achieved progress but should in the future be supplemented with new approaches that might better address cross-media pollution transfers, the need for cost-effective alternatives, and methods of controlling pollution from dispersed or nonpoint sources of pollution.

The Act states that –

[52] Prepared by James E. McCarthy, Specialist in Environmental Policy, Resources, Science, and Industry Division.

> it is the policy of the United States that pollution should be prevented or reduced at the source whenever feasible; pollution that cannot be prevented should be recycled in an environmentally safe manner, whenever feasible; pollution that cannot be prevented or recycled should be treated in an environmentally safe manner whenever feasible; and disposal or other release into the environment should be employed only as a last resort and should be conducted in an environmentally safe manner [§6602(b)].

These principles were adopted 15-20 years after the development of a complex regulatory structure that governs emissions to the air, water, and land separately, however, and their adoption has had little effect on the day-to-day functioning of environmental regulatory authorities. Further, EPA and its state counterparts are essentially reactive agencies, with little authority to require the use of cleaner production methods or to require the adoption of "environmentally preferable" products. Given the fundamental respect for private property that permeates American society and an economic system that values free enterprise above most competing values, EPA and state environmental agencies are unlikely ever to have authority to regulate production methods or production decisions, except in extreme cases where a production method or product can be demonstrated to pose an unreasonable risk to human health or the environment.[53]

Pollution Prevention Tools in the United States and Internationally

Given these constraints, the government's role in pollution prevention has been limited largely to research, information gathering, and information dissemination. Tools such as the Toxics Release Inventory and voluntary programs in which industry commits to reduce pollution beyond the requirements of law ("beyond compliance") in return for public recognition and use of an EPA-developed symbol are perhaps the Agency's most widely recognized tools.

---

[53] There are, in fact, some cases in which EPA has been given and has exercised pollution prevention authority, for example in banning the manufacture and sale of asbestos products or of DDT, or prohibiting the use of lead in gasoline. Several statutes, including the Clean Air Act and the Federal Insecticide, Fungicide, and Rodenticide Act, provide some such authority. The broadest authority is probably that provided in the Toxic Substances Control Act (P.L. 94-469), which gives EPA the power to control "unreasonable risks" to human health and the environment by prohibiting or limiting production or distribution of harmful substances or products containing them. Use of this authority has been rare.

In recent years, another pollution prevention tool has been the Supplemental Environmental Project (SEP). SEPs are environmentally beneficial projects that may be proposed by a violator during the settlement of an enforcement action. In FY 1998, EPA settlements produced 221 SEPs valued at $90.8 million. Over the 1996-1998 fiscal years, 20% of all judicial and administrative penalty orders included SEPs. SEPs are often used as a pollution prevention tool: in reporting on its FY1998 enforcement accomplishments, EPA estimated that "60% of SEPs offered human health or worker protection benefits, while 52% offered ecosystem protection."[54]

Extended Producer Responsibility

There are other possible approaches that combine regulation and pollution prevention. The most frequently discussed is an approach referred to as "Extended Producer Responsibility" (EPR). EPR is a term applied to efforts in Europe, Japan, and elsewhere that hold producers of certain products responsible for managing them at the end of their useful life. This management may be accomplished individually, by requiring manufacturers to take products back after use, or collectively, by allowing take back or recycling to be managed by an industry-wide organization. Perhaps the best known example of EPR is the Green Dot system for packaging recovery and recycling established in Germany by Duales System Deutschland (DSD). Under the German Ordinance on the Avoidance of Packaging Waste, adopted in 1991 and fully implemented in 1993, packaging must be recovered and reused or recycled by retailers and manufacturers. Since retailers did not wish to collect used packages, manufacturers established a consortium to operate a separate collection system for used packaging throughout Germany. (The Green Dot, or recycling symbol, identifies those packages included in the system.)

This Dual System collects material for recycling curbside or at drop-off locations in much the same way local governments or private organizations do in the United States, but the system operates nationwide, and is paid for by fees that the manufacturer or packager gives to DSD. These fees are based on the cost of recovering and recycling specific materials (glass, plastic, paper, etc.). Thus, manufacturers have an incentive to minimize packaging waste, since they must pay for its recovery; and packages that are not recyclable are forced out of the system.

---

[54] U.S. EPA. Office of Enforcement and Compliance Assurance. FY98 OECA Accomplishments Report, June 1999, p. 4.

Many European countries and Japan have adopted systems similar to Germany's Green Dot for managing their packaging waste, and the concept is now being applied in Germany and elsewhere to automobiles, electronic equipment, and other products. By returning products for reuse or recycling, these EPR systems provide incentives for the design of products that are easily reused or recycled and minimize the disposal of solid and hazardous waste.

There are many sources of information on pollution prevention and extended producer responsibility. Two comprehensive sources are the EPA Office of Pollution Prevention Website [http://www.epa.gov/p2/] and the National Pollution Prevention Roundtable [http://www.p2.org]. For information on extended producer responsibility, the Organization for Economic Cooperation and Development's Website [http://www.oecd.org/env/] is searchable using the term "Extended Producer Responsibility." Among OECD publications is a 1996 report on EPR policies in the OECD member countries.

ENVIRONMENTAL MANAGEMENT SYSTEMS AND AUDITS[55]

Over the last 10 years, corporations and governments have given a great deal of attention to the use of environmental management systems (EMS) as a tool to lessen environmental impacts and improve compliance with environmental laws. The most prominent efforts to facilitate the use of EMSs have been those of the International Organization for Standardization (ISO), which has developed a series of standards for environmental management systems referred to as the ISO 14000 standards.

Voluntary Industry Standards

ISO is a nongovernmental, international, industry-based organization. Its U.S. counterpart, the American National Standards Institute (ANSI), has a long history - as does ISO - of setting voluntary industry and product standards to facilitate both domestic and international commerce.

[55] Prepared by James E. McCarthy, Specialist in Environmental Policy, Resources, Science and Industry Division.

In the 1990s, ISO (with ANSI participation) developed a set of standards covering environmental management, environmental auditing, life cycle assessment, environmental labeling, and environmental performance. To be certified or registered under these standards, an organization must demonstrate that it has an Environmental Management System in conformity with ISO 14001. Conformity with ISO 14001 indicates that a company or organization has a system in place for setting environmental goals, auditing performance, and taking corrective action. But the company or organization is free to set its own goals; thus, compliance with ISO 14001 does not necessarily certify environmental excellence. Furthermore, the absence of any meaningful public reporting requirement in the standard means that outsiders have no way of judging a company's environmental performance under the standard.

Thus, compliance with ISO 14001, often discussed as a new method of stimulating improved environmental performance, is probably not, in its current form, a substitute for environmental regulation. But many feel it has the potential to improve corporate performance and benefit the environment.

Environmental Audits

The same may be said for a related tool, the environmental audit. Environmental audits presume that there are environmental regulations against which to measure a company's performance. In the absence of regulations, an audit would be relatively meaningless.

Audits have been used extensively in the corporate world as a means of improving environmental performance. A 1995 survey by Price Waterhouse found that 75% of 369 companies who responded conducted such audits and another 8% planned to do so.

Some argue that audits would be even more widely used were it not for fear that they may provide evidence that could be used against the company in court or in other enforcement proceedings. As a result, there has been a lively debate throughout the 1990s as to whether state and federal governments should consider information collected in audits to be "privileged," or inadmissible in enforcement proceedings. About 20 states have provided some such privilege for environmental audit information, and some states offer immunity from civil and criminal penalties to persons and entities reporting violations detected in such audits, provided that violations detected are promptly reported and corrected.

U.S. EPA and the Department of Justice have adopted policies restricting the role of audit information in enforcement proceedings and reducing penalties for voluntary disclosure of violations; but they oppose legislation that they believe would limit their discretion in such matters. Such legislation was the subject of congressional hearings in the mid-1990s, but now appears to have less support.

Chapter 8

APPENDIX A: SELECTED READINGS

Jonathan H. Adler, ed., *Ecology, Liberty & Property: A Free Market Environmental Reader* (Washington, D.C.: Competitive Enterprise Institute, 2000)

Terry Anderson, ed.. *Breaking the Environmental Policy Gridlock* (Stanford, CA: Hoover Institution Press, 1997)

The Aspen Institute, *The Alternative Path* (1996) [at http://www.aspeninst.org/dir/eee/altpath.html]

Ronald Bailey, ed., *Earth Report 2000: Revisiting the True State of the Planet* (New York: McGraw-Hill, 2000)

The Business Roundtable, *Toward Smarter Regulation* (Washington, D.C.: The Business Roundtable, updated 1995)

Carnage Commission on Science, Technology, and Government, *Risk and the Environment: Improving Regulatory Decision Making* (New York: Carnegie Corporation, 1993)

Marian R. Chertow and Daniel C. Esty, *Thinking Ecologically: the Next Generation of Environmental Policy* (New Haven: Yale University Press, 1997)

Robert W. Crandall, et. al., *An Agenda for Federal Regulatory Reform* (Washington, D.C.: American Enterprise Institute for Public Policy Research and The Brookings Institution, 1997)

Environmental Protection Agency, National Center for Environmental Economics, [http://www.epa.gov/economics/]. See, for example, Robert Anderson, "Economic Savings from Using Economic Incentives for Environmental Pollution Control" and Robert C. Anderson and Andrew Q. Lohof, *The United States Experience with Economic Incentives in Environmental Pollution Control Policy*.

The Environmental Protection System in Transition: Toward a More Desirable Future (Washington, D.C.: Center for Strategic and International Studies. 1998)

Peter Humber, *Hard Green: Saving the Environment from the Environmentalists: A Conservative Manifesto* (New York: Basic Books, 1999)

National Academy of Public Administration, *environment.gov: Transforming Environmental Protection for the 21st Century* (Washington, D.C.: National Academy of Public Administration, 2000)

Wallace E. Oates, ed., *The RFF Reader in Environmental and Resource Management* (Washington, D.C.: Resources for the Future, 1999)

The Presidential/Congressional Commission on Risk Assessment and Risk Management, *Framework for Environmental Health Risk Management* (1997) at [http://www.riskworld.com/]

Research and Policy Committee of the Committee for Economic Development, *Modernizing Government Regulation: The Need for Action* (New York: Committee for Economic Development, 1998)

Philip Shabecoff, *Earth Rising: American environmentalism in the 21st century* (Washington, D.C.: Island Press, 2000).

Irwin M. Stelzer and Paul R. Portney, Making Environmental Policy: Two Views (Washington, D.C.: The AEI Press, 1998). ((25th Anniversary Special Issue," *Journal of Environmental Economics and Management*, 39 (May 2000).

World Wide Web Virtual Library "SUSTAINABLE DEVELOPMENT," at [http://www.ulb.ac.be/ceese/meta/sustvl.html]

INDEX

L

M

N

O

P

R